ARBA
Pictorial History of Roadbuilding
By Charles W. Wixom

**A publication of the
American Road
Builders' Association
525 School Street, S.W.
Washington, D.C. 20024**

FOREWORD

The American Road Builders' Association, founded in 1902, is composed of business organizations and individuals with interests in all phases of transportation development. This book deals with one, very important phase—road-building.

Many members of ARBA have played important roles in the construction of the national highway system. The book is a reflection of their pride in the work they have done.

This is a book to be enjoyed. The pictures and text tell a fascinating story of men and machines at work. If pride and a love of the work show through in the publication, it is both intentional and inevitable.

James A. Nelson
Vice President and General
Manager,
E.D. Etnyre and Company
President, ARBA

Ray W. Burgess
Director of Public Works,
Baton Rouge, Louisiana
Chairman, Editorial Advisory
Committee

CONTENTS

INTRODUCTION

Anyone who attempts the task of writing a history of American roads faces the problem of deciding where to start—and where to stop.

The story of roads is closely intertwined with the whole story of the American people. If we define roads broadly enough to include Indian trails, we could begin even before the European settlement of America with a discussion of the nomadic habits of some tribes which, almost literally, lived on the road. From this point, the narrative possibilities expand almost without limit to include the growth of trade, Westward expansion, military movements, the development of tourism, and so forth.

With some reluctance, we have turned away from the challenge of writing a book that would explain the relationship of roads to everything else. This is not a history of travel, or a saga of economic development. Our purpose is simply to tell the story of roadbuilding. Again, there is a deliberate narrowing of the subject matter, for which no apologies are made.

The available literature on this subject is surprisingly sparse and scattered. Official summaries of progress dwell heavily on tax revenues and budget outlays, vehicle-miles of travel, the economic impact of better roads, and inter-governmental relationships. Technical papers describe the materials and techniques used in the construction of roads. But not much has been written about the men who built the roads, and there are significant gaps in the history of machinery development. For the reader who can devote only a little time to the subject, pictures tell the story best.

The pictures in this book were selected from many sources. One of the great satisfactions in the production of the book has been the discovery of illustrations in unexpected places. For example, the line drawings of early Twentieth Century construction machinery are the work of Walt Pittman of El Monte, California, a veteran equipment operator and steam equipment buff. He restores steam equipment, builds scale models, and combines artistic ability with a working knowledge of the machinery. A similar thrill came with the receipt of a box filled with old, unclassified photos from the Nebraska Department of Roads. They breathe the atmosphere of day-to-day operations in the 1920's.

Hundreds of people helped. The acknowledgements here can only mention a few of the most outstanding.

Perhaps the richest lode of all is the collection of old Bureau of Public Roads photographs in the National Archives. The Library of Congress, the Smithsonian Institution and the Federal Department of Transportation are other important sources of historic roadbuilding photographs. The Federal Highway Administration's collection of historic oil paintings, now being refurbished, is a unique resource.

Several State highway agencies have published historical books and booklets. One of the most extensive and best is "Florida Trails to Turnpikes," written by Baynard Kendrick for the Florida State Road Department's Golden Anniversary, in 1964, with the support of highway industry groups. In the booklet category, Virginia's road history, which begins with an account of transportation in colonial days, is particularly worthy of mention.

The State highway and transportation departments were especially helpful in providing contemporary photographs. Some of them have the good fortune to employ staff photographers of the highest order of professional skill. Among those of nationally recognized stature are Ercol Acri of the Pennsylvania Department of Transportation and Johnnie M. Gray of the Arkansas Highway Department. Many others labor in anonymity. The back end papers in this book were made from a photo taken by an anonymous South Carolina Highway Department photographer. The Arizona Transportation Department magazine, "Arizona Highways," enjoys an international reputation for photographic excellence, and the magazine itself is preeminent among successful governmental publications.

The late E.H. Holt, a former President of ARBA and Vice President of the Barber-Greene Company, gave special help and encouragement during the early stages of research, and suggested several leads within the construction equipment manufacturing industry. The Construction Industry Manufacturers Association relayed our appeal for help to the entire industry. While the industry response was virtually total, special appreciation is due Jerry Cook of the

Caterpillar Tractor Co. for his constructive criticism of material related to earthmoving. Highway contractors responded generously to an appeal for old photographs. Many old snapshots, unfortunately, were too faded or blurred for quality reproduction. The most responsive of all was Dale Capon of S.J. Groves & Co., with photos from dozens of job sites.

Photographs were submitted by county and municipal officials, planning and design firms and others. Special mention must be made of the contribution of William H. Shank, P.E., of the American Canal & Transportation Center, York, Pennsylvania. During the late 1960's, Mr. Shank served as public relations manager for Buchart-Horn. The consulting firm distributed a series of remarkable historical booklets written by Mr. Shank. He has permitted us to borrow from his excellent "Indian Trails to Super Highways."

ARBA Past President Paul Reinhold of Pittsburgh, Pennsylvania, shared with us his unique collection of transportation memorabilia.

At an early stage, we sought the advice of C.D. (Cap) Curtiss, former Commissioner of Public Roads and former Assistant to the Executive Vice President of ARBA. His keen memory and analytic mind put our research on the proper path. Former Federal Highway Administrator Francis C. Turner read an early draft of the text and made many valuable suggestions.

The work has proceeded under the overview of a special ARBA committee with singular talents. Under the enthusiastic chairmanship of Ray Burgess, Director of Public Works, Baton Rouge, La., the committee included a leading publisher, Donald V. Buttenheim, Chairman of the Board, Buttenheim Publishing Company; a veteran local government engineer, Harold Absher, Washington County, Illinois, Superintendent of Highways; a bridge expert, Robert F. Wellner, Bethlehem Steel Corporation; a highway contractor and transportation history buff, Richard R. Stander, Mansfield Asphalt Paving Company, Mansfield, Ohio, and three members with backgrounds so extensive and eclectic as to defy classification—E.M. Johnson, President of The Asphalt Institute; Wilbur S. Smith, President, Wilbur Smith and Associates, and Harold L. Michael, Head, Transportation and Urban Engineering, School of Civil Engineering, Purdue University.

The secretary of this ARBA committee was Randolph Russell. He has been not only an active participant in the entire project, but also a positive and thoroughly professional guide. He is a skillful editor, with extensive contacts throughout the entire highway industry and an innate talent for diplomacy. All of these good qualities have been at the disposal of the author. ARBA's Executive Vice President, Daniel J. Hanson, Sr., has given this project his personal encouragement at every turn. His enthusiasm and leadership has been invaluable.

Production of this book was supervised by Jack Horner for Kal, Merrick & Salan. His contributions went well beyond the basic requirements of his assignment. He read the text critically, assisted in the acquisition of certain key photographs, and in many other ways contributed to the attractiveness and accuracy of the book. The design and layout reflect the professional skill, dedication and imagination of Susan Laird Jenkins of the Kal, Merrick & Salan staff. These talents have been admirably complemented by James Witt and the staff of W.M. Brown & Son, Inc., the printer.

Two persons deserve particular credit for contributions of a type too often unsung. Billie Ray Perry provided helpful staff support, while Denise Pendleton typed several drafts of manuscript with uncommon patience and competence. My wife and sons helped and encouraged me continuously, often in small but important ways.

For the assistance of all of these, and many others, the author is deeply appreciative. Any errors and omissions that may remain exist despite their efforts and are my responsibility.

Charles W. Wixom

Washington, D.C.
May, 1975

CHAPTER 1

INDIAN TRAILS AND COLONIAL EXTENSIONS

Before 1607, America was a vast primeval forest from the East Coast to the Mississippi River, impassable except for rivers, streams and game trails. The game trails served as footways for the commerce and wars of the Indian nations that predated the white man's landing. These were the first roads of America. They provided the basic structure for communication among the many Indian nations; they were the links for American society as it then existed. These trails, rarely more than two feet wide, and often impenetrable beyond that width, twisted through dense forests along the path of least resistance that the originating bison and buck had chosen. They were rutted by moccasined feet and pounding hooves and became streamlets in heavy rain.

Following such trails, the traveler found, according to Archer B. Hulbert in his 20-volumes on American roads, "incessant change of scenery, the continued surprises, the objects passed unseen yet not unguessed, those half-seen through a leafy vista amid the shimmering green; the pathway just in front very plain, but twenty feet beyond as absolutely hidden from your eyes as though it were a thousand miles away . . ." The "vista presented varied only with the altitude save where hidden by the foliage. We do not choose the old 'ridge roads' today (in 1900) for the view to be obtained, and we look continually up while the old time traveler so often looked down.

"But the one characteristic to which, ordinarily, there was no exception, was the narrowness of these ancient routes. The Indian did not travel in single file because there was advantage in that formation; it was because his only routes were trails which he never widened or improved; and these would, ordinarily, admit only of one such person as broke them open.

"Thus, very narrow, exceedingly crooked, often overgrown, worn a foot or more into the ground, lay the routes on which white men built roads which have become historic.

"The first phase of road-making (if it can be dignified by such a title) was the broadening of the Indian path by the mere passing of wider loads over it. The beginning of the pack-horse era was announced by the need of greater quantities of merchandise and provisions in the West, to which these paths led.

"The heavier the freight tied on either side of the pack-horse, the more were

the bushes bruised and worn away and the more the bed of the trail was tracked and trampled. The increasing of the fur trade with the East at the beginning of the last half of the Eighteenth Century necessitated heavier loads of the trading ponies both 'going in' and 'coming out'—as the pioneers were wont to say."

Formal road-building began in this country shortly after the founding of the colonies as the earliest settlers provided for streets in their cities.

In 1632, the General Assembly of Virginia passed the first road law of the new colonies: "Highways shall be layd out in such convenient places as requisite accordings as the governor and counsell or the commissioners for the monthlie corts shall appoint, or accordings as the parishioners of every parish shall agree."

As early as 1639, the Massachusetts Bay Colony established provisions for both right-of-way and crude construction specifications: "Whereas the highways in this jurisdiction have not been layd out with such conveniency for travelers as were fit, nor as was intended by this court, but that in some places they have felt too straight, and in

other places travellers are forced to go far about, it is therefore, ordered, that all highways shall be layd out before the next general court, so as may be with most ease and safety for travelers; and for this end every town shall choose two or three men, who shall join with two or three of the next town, and they shall have power to lay out the highways in each town where they may be most convenient; and those which are so deputed shall have power to lay out the highways where they may be most convenient, not withstanding any man's propriety, or any corne ground, so as it occasion not the pulling down of any man's house, or laying open any garden or orchard; and in common grounds, or where the soil is wet or miry, they shall lay out the ways the wider as 6, or 8, or 10 rods or more in common grounds."

Such laws, plus similar acts in New York and Pennsylvania, provided for such road building as existed through most of the Seventeenth Century. William Penn extended some highways beyond the city limits of Philadelphia in 1683 and made the governor and provincial assembly responsible for "all necessary roads and highways in the province." In 1692, Pennsylvania gave its townships jurisdiction over roads.

Nicholson Hollow Road, Virginia, as it appeared in 1935. The dense foliage is gone, but otherwise the boulder-and-tree-strewn "road" resembles those of 300 years ago.

The "Old Mine Road" is thought to be the oldest highway on the continent. It covered a distance of 104 miles from Sussex to Warren Counties in New Jersey on to Kingston, New York. It is said that the Dutch built this road between 1620 and 1650 in order to carry copper ore from inland mines to New York harbors, but abandoned it when New Jersey was surrendered to the British in 1664. As late as 1800, John Adams is

said to have regarded it as part of the best route between Philadelphia and Boston.

The need to exchange thoughts as well as goods impelled early extensions of men and their letters beyond their settlements. As early as 1639 Plymouth was linked to Boston by a path, a stretch of which later became part of the "Boston Post Road." By 1673, the Boston Post Road extended to New York City.

Otherwise, travel through the colonies followed Indian routes for trapping, hunting, and trading; such as, the Allegheny Path which ran from Philadelphia across Pennsylvania to the present site of Pittsburgh and beyond. The Seneca Trail twisted from the south branch of the Potomac River through rugged West Virginia into the little Kanawha River valley and on to the Ohio River, near present-day Parkersburg. So many animals, Indians, settlers, explorers, trappers, and soldiers traveled this trail, and wore it so deeply into the soil, that traces of it could still be located 200 years later. By 1726, settlers were pushing to the western Alleghenies, one trail reaching to Bunker Hill (W. Va.) The first road formally laid west—probably little more than a blazed trail—was begun by the Ohio Company, a party of Virginia gentlemen, on the condition that 100 families should be settled in two years on 200,000 acres granted them on the Ohio River between Monongahela and the Kanawha.

As continental America was penetrated and its riches uncovered, contentions

The "Old Mine Road," New Jersey, was built between 1620 and 1650. In 1940, when this picture was taken, parts of the road were still in use.

for this wealth arose, and with them the motivations for the earliest extensions of inland road-building. The French had established fortifications inland in the territories, following the routes of their trappers in the forest of the old northwest. In 1753, upon news that French troops had penetrated into the Ohio River Valley (then part of Virginia), the Colonial government dispatched young George Washington to inform the French commander that he was not to build a fort at the confluence of the Ohio and the Monongahela, the site of Pittsburgh. Washington traveled in three wintery months by horse and canoe from Williamsburg, Virginia to Cumberland, Maryland, in part following the Ohio Company Road.

At Cumberland, Washington was told by the French that they had no intention of leaving the Ohio Valley, and he carried this news back to Virginia. A year later, war with the French seemed inevitable (the French and Indian war indeed resulted in large part from the French determination to stay), and the Colonial government dispatched Washington

Stafford County, Virginia, 1912.

again over the same road, this time with 200 men and 10 swivel guns.

For this trip it was probably necessary to widen and straighten the road, perhaps the first extensive use of corduroy roads in the country. To "corduroy" a road, men cut timbers and laid them contiguously side by side to provide a firm foundation over soft or boggy spots. Defeated in the skirmish that ensued upon his eventual arrival, Washington returned east and became an aid to General Edward Braddock who in 1755, with 2,200 men and heavy artillery, set out again, determined to remove the French from Fort Duquesne. Braddock also took 150 wagons and horse teams, obtained by Benjamin Franklin for the mission. For this extensive force and heavy equipment, Braddock sent several hundred men ahead of the main body to cut a 12-foot-wide wagon and artillery road—the first long, major road on the continent. The detachment felled trees, bridged creeks, and laid causeways across the swamps, crossing eight major mountains and virgin forests. Washington complained that the road makers delayed the Army because they were "stopping to level every mole hill." Finally arriving within a few miles of Fort Duquesne, Braddock's force walked into a French-Indian ambush, was

Braddock's Road.

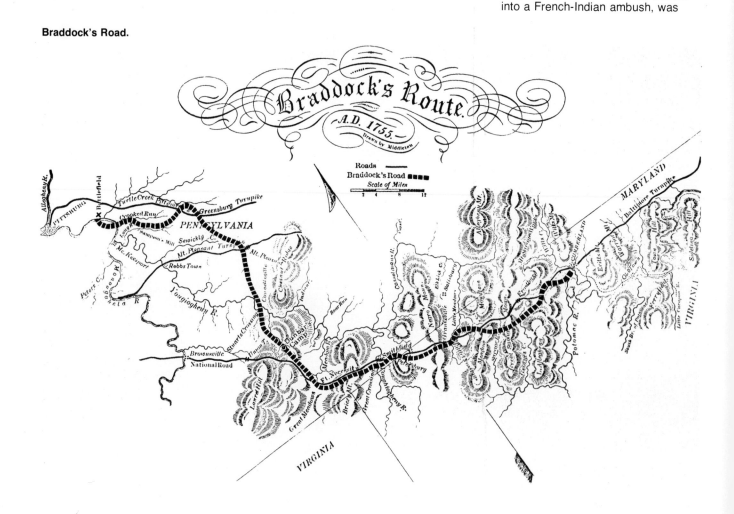

soundly beaten, Braddock killed, and the remaining force retreated along the roadway they had built.

In 1758, to make up for Braddock's failure, General John Forbes was dispatched with still another force against Fort Duquesne. Forbes chose a route through Pennsylvania by way of what is now Bedford and Ligonier, partly following a wagon trail opened in 1754 to Bedford, along the top of Allegheny Ridge. When Forbes reached Fort Duquesne, he found the fort abandoned. By 1759, Forbes Road was opened from Philadelphia to the site of Pittsburgh. Although Braddock Road meanwhile had become "filled with a brushwood, by the sprouts from the old stumps," thus were opened the first two major westward roads.

Daniel Boone made the first important penetration west of the Alleghenies. In May of 1769, Boone pushed into Kentucky with a party of six men, including his brother, beyond the mountains and into the Ohio River country, where they lived and hunted for more than six months. In December, Indians attacked them, capturing Boone and separating him from his brother, who eluded the attackers. Boone later escaped and lived alone in the wilderness for four months.

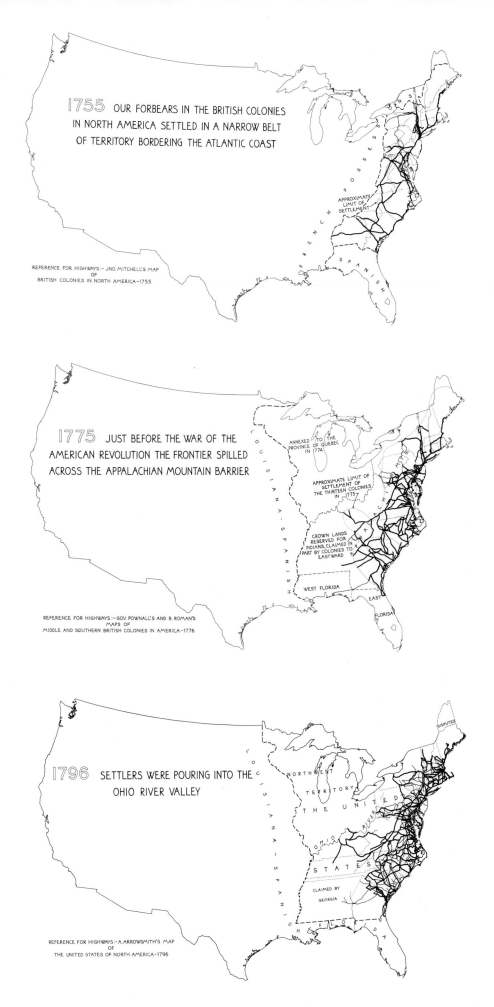

1755 OUR FORBEARS IN THE BRITISH COLONIES IN NORTH AMERICA SETTLED IN A NARROW BELT OF TERRITORY BORDERING THE ATLANTIC COAST

REFERENCE FOR HIGHWAYS:- JNO. MITCHELL'S MAP OF BRITISH COLONIES IN NORTH AMERICA-1755

1775 JUST BEFORE THE WAR OF THE AMERICAN REVOLUTION THE FRONTIER SPILLED ACROSS THE APPALACHIAN MOUNTAIN BARRIER

REFERENCE FOR HIGHWAYS:- GOV. POWNALL'S AND B. ROMAN'S MAPS OF MIDDLE AND SOUTHERN BRITISH COLONIES IN AMERICA-1776

1796 SETTLERS WERE POURING INTO THE OHIO RIVER VALLEY

REFERENCE FOR HIGHWAYS - A. ARROWSMITH'S MAP OF THE UNITED STATES OF NORTH AMERICA-1796

Noting his loneliness, he wrote later, "One day I undertook a tour through the country, and diversity and beauties of nature I met within this charming season, expelled every gloomy and vexacious thought. Just at the close of day, the gales retired, and left the place to the disposal of a profound calm. Not a breeze shook the most tremulous leaf. I had gained the summit of a commanding ridge, and, looking round with astonishing delight, beheld the ample plains, the beauteous tracts below. On the other hand, I surveyed the famous river Ohio, that rolled in silent dignity marking the western boundary of Kentucky within conceivable grandeur."

On the 27th of July, he wrote, "to my great felicity," he ran across his brother and they returned to the Cumberland River where they explored until March of 1771. Boone returned home determined to bring "my family as soon as possible to live in Kentucky, which I esteemed a

Boone's Wilderness Road, 1775.

second paradise, at the risk of my life and fortune." He did, commissioned by the Transylvania Company in 1775, set up trade with the Indians in the wilderness bounded by the Ohio, Kentucky, and Cumberland Rivers, and established Boonesborough there, which became the destination of the Cumberland Road or the Wilderness Road. By 1792, the state of Kentucky was formed; by the turn of the century, 200,000 settlers had followed Boone into the Kentucky country.

CHAPTER 2
CITIES AND PIKES

By 1790, the population of this young country exceeded 3,000,000. About 1,000,000 lived in New England. There were 550,000 residents in New York, New Jersey and Pennsylvania, while 1,850,000 persons made their homes in the South Atlantic states, ranging from Delaware to Florida. Virginia was by far the most populous state, with about 690,000 people.

The early settlements arose along waterways, especially in the South, so transportation generally, and especially freight transportation, was by water. However, as the planters moved inland, they had to devise means to get their crops to market. Tobacco was frequently moved to the nearest water shipping point on the so-called "rolling roads" over which the oxen pulled tobacco packed into huge drums, usually about four feet in diameter.

As the towns and cities grew, so did commerce between them. By 1750, mail was being carried between New York and Philadelphia once a week in the summer and twice a month in the winter.

Mail service reached from Boston to Charleston, S.C., in 1763. By 1790, there were 1,800 miles of post routes in the United States, and the mail moved five times a week between New York and Philadelphia.

The use of wheeled vehicles developed slowly. Before the Revolution, coaches were seldom seen except in and near the cities and towns. In the countryside, wheels usually meant wagons. The use of wagons required the widening of country roads, but resulted in little other improvement in their quality. Boston is said to have counted 22 wheeled vehicles on its streets in 1768. By 1790, the vehicle population was 145. The vehicle growth in Philadelphia was somewhat greater. There were 38 vehicles there in 1760, 827 in 1794.

In 1750, in Lancaster County, Pennsylvania, a revolution in land transportation arose. It took the form of a wagon, rugged and ungainly in appearance, constructed of a bed of white oak planks, one-half to five-eighths of an inch thick. It was 26 feet long, 11 feet high and

weighed about 3,000 pounds. The end gates were sloped to prevent cargo from spilling. Four-inch wide wheels helped the wagon move over rough and muddy roads. These lumbering carriers could haul as much as three tons and, where roads were decent, travel as much as 20 miles a day. This was the famous Conestoga wagon.

With wagons of this size, the wagoner was positioned on the left side of the wagon and—where the road was wide enough to give him any choice—usually preferred to keep to the right in order to have a clear view of the road ahead. This "wagoner's choice" was the beginning of right-hand driving in the United States. However, it was nowhere official until formally adopted in New Jersey in 1813.

Passengers traveled in smaller wagons, built without springs of any kind. In the 1760's, a bone-jolting "speed run" between New York and Philadelphia required a day and a half. Increased commerce and the use of wheeled vehicles urgently demanded improved roads.

However, much of the commercial travel was through territory where the local governments had few resources for, and perhaps limited interest in, road improvements. The partial solution was the turnpike system.

The principle of the turnpike was simple: Block the road until the traveler paid his tariff. The blocking was done with a pike on a swivel—thus "turnpike."

Virginia's legislature passed an act in 1785 providing for the erection of turnpike poles. The idea was probably borrowed from England, where the system had been used at least 20 years earlier. The first recorded turnpike was on a route from Alexandria to Snigger's and Vesta's Gaps, in the Blue Ridge. Though fares were collected, few improvements were made. After ten years, the legislature was informed that the turnpike required "an artificial bed of pounded or broken stone." As this was felt to be too costly for the public treasury, the legislature authorized a private firm, the "Fairfax and Loudon Turnpike Road Company" to incorporate and reconstruct the old turnpike from Little River to Alexandria. An 1805 successor, "The Little River Turnpike Company," operated the road on a toll basis for more than 90 years.

Two Connecticut toll roads, the old Mohigan Road between New London and Norwich and the Post Road in Greenwich, were converted from free roads to toll roads in 1792. Toll gates were set up on the Reisterstown Road, near Baltimore, in 1793, and on the road through Tennessee's Cumberland Gap in 1801.

This "Flying Machine" made the run from New York to Philadelphia in a day and a half in the 1770's.

An early toll gate and toll house.

The famous Lancaster Pike was in another class altogether, fully deserving to be called the first extensive, carefully planned and constructed road in the United States. As one historian has noted, its construction "heralded the dawn of a new day in roadbuilding." The Pike was built between 1792 and 1794, connecting the cities of Philadelphia and Lancaster, Pennsylvania, a distance of 62 miles. The specifications called for a roadway 50 feet wide, with the 24-foot center section to be "an artificial road, bedded with wood, stone or gravel, and any other hard substance, well compacted together, a sufficient depth to secure a solid foundation . . . faced with gravel, or stone pounded, or other small hard substance, in such a manner as to secure a firm and . . . an even surface, rising toward the middle by a gradual arch."

The road was cut through a densely wooded wilderness. As the line of supply was long, the builders improved their camp menus by hunting and fishing. The aggregate, too, was whatever could be found locally, including local broken limestone and gravel of many sizes. Considering the difficulties, the builders did well to complete the road for $465,000, or $7,500 a mile.

There were thirteen toll gates on the road. The toll structure might be termed a horsepower-axle tariff; the more horses and axles one had, the higher the rate. A horse and rider could travel 10 miles for a sixteenth of a dollar, but a one-horse two-wheeled sulky was charged twice that. A four-wheeled wagon drawn by two horses would be assessed a quarter of a dollar, and a four-horse vehicle 50 percent more.

By the 1830's, Pennsylvania had chartered more than 80 turnpike companies with routes extending 2,400 miles. Turnpikes also boomed in other states. In this same period, New York had 278 companies, capitalized at $11,000,000 and operating about 4,000 miles of road. In the early decades of the Nineteenth Century, about 3,700 miles of turnpike were built in New England, at a cost of about $6,500,000.

Although these roads were privately financed, they were strongly influenced by government. Virginia, in 1816, established a policy of supervising turnpike

Winter on the Philadelphia and Lancaster Pike.

construction through an official Board of Public Works. Other state governments also regulated the construction and maintenance of turnpikes. It was a situation analogous to that of the public utilities of the present era, with financing and operating responsibility assumed by the private sector, under the watchful eye of government.

In the evolution of the early American roads, bridges usually came last, probably for fiscal reasons. At a time when unskilled labor could be hired for literally pennies a day, it may often have been cheaper to operate a ferry than to build a bridge.

Roman engineers of the second and first centuries B.C. had solved the problems of designing a stone arch bridge capable of bearing heavy weight. The Old London Bridge, completed in 1209, and the Ponte Vecchio in Florence, Italy, carried heavy shops and other buildings before the discovery of America.

The basic principle of the truss has been recognized nearly as far back in history as the arch. It is, simply, that the triangle is the one and only geometric form which cannot be distorted. (Of course, the strength of materials and joints must be considered.) A simple type of bridge can be built by running a pair of ladder-like framed structures from pier to pier and then placing the roadway beams crosswise between them. Adding diagonal members to the framed structures converts rectangular shapes into triangles.

Such a chain of triangles is known, generally, as a truss. The form was known as early as the 13th century.

Early American bridge builders employed both the arch and the truss, sometimes in the same bridge. A Newburyport, Mass., carpenter, Timothy Palmer, patented an arch-truss bridge in 1792, and built numerous bridges to this design. His most famous accomplishment, the so-called Permanent Bridge over the Schuylkill River at Philadelphia (1806) was enclosed by roof and sidings—an early example of the covered bridge.

Another remarkable arch-truss bridge, The Colossus, was built by German immigrant Lewis Wernwag in 1812, a few miles downstream from the Permanent Bridge. The Colossus was a single trussed arch with a clear span of 340 feet, built of laminated timbers.

Covered bridges became very popular in American roadbuilding. Although subject to attack by fire, flood and termites, wooden bridges protected from the weather proved almost incredibly long-lived. Some remained in use for more than a century. In 1963, it was reported that 1,342 were still standing in the United States.

Although early builders combined the arch and truss designs, presumably as a sort of fail-safe device, the combination is not very efficient. Improved truss designs came into use in response to the requirement for better bridges to bear the heavy moving loads of railroad trains.

During the 1840's, cast iron gradually joined timber as a basic material for railroad bridges. It soon gave way to wrought iron, which serves better under tension. As railroad weights increased, bridge builders turned gradually to steel bridge designs.

The Eagle Hotel, a noted stop on the Lancaster Pike in the 1790's. The hotel was 17 miles from Philadelphia.

CHAPTER 3

ZANE'S TRACE AND THE NATIONAL ROAD

Ebenezer Zane was a man with big ideas. He also had the money to put his ideas into action. One of his big ideas was Federal aid for highways. In this case, the recipient of the Federal aid was Zane himself.

Zane cashed in on knowing the territory—in his case, the Ohio Territory. As Zane knew, there was considerable boat traffic of a one-way nature on the Ohio and Mississippi Rivers. The boats were sold along with their freight at the end of the line, and the boatmen would return overland to what is now Pittsburgh and begin over again.

Zane proposed to cut a road from Pittsburgh, then the western terminus of the improved road running through Pennsylvania, to a connection with the road from the South, known as the Natchez Trace.

In 1796, Zane petitioned Congress for Federal assistance in the development of his road. He was quite modest in his request. He asked only for landing sites for ferries at the crossings of the Muskingum, Hocking and Scioto Rivers together with "such expenses as may be incurred in surveying and laying off such lots of land." Congress gave him a

A return route of Mississippi boatmen, the Natchez Trace, ran 460 miles through dense forests.

square mile at each of the three sites. With that encouragement, Zane opened his road and established ferries at each of the rivers. Eventually, the route was extended until it stretched 200 miles and reached the site of Maysville, Kentucky. In the process, Zane expedited the settlement of much of southern Ohio and became even wealthier.

The population of Ohio reached 60,000 by 1800. At that time, this was the minimum population required for a territory to petition for statehood. With the active encouragement of President Thomas Jefferson, Ohio became a state in 1802. One of the provisions of the Ohio statehood act reads:

> "One-twentieth of the net proceeds of the lands lying within said state sold by Congress shall be applied to the laying-out and making of public roads leading from the navigable waters emptying into the Atlantic, to the Ohio, to the said state and through same, such roads to be laid out under the authority of Congress, with the consent of the several states through which the roads shall pass."

Zane's Trace ferry.

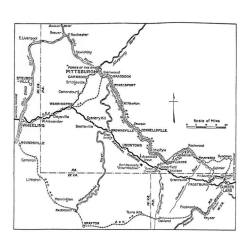

The Cumberland (National) Road.

The Ohio act, the first providing for Federal aid for road construction across state lines, led to the passage of legislation establishing the first true national road to the west.

Conceived by George Washington as a route to the Northwest Territories, the idea of the national road appealed to both Virginia and Massachusetts speculators and attracted the support of Thomas Jefferson, Henry Clay and James Madison.

In 1805, President Jefferson appointed a committee to determine the best route from east coast ports into Ohio. The committee recommended that "a good road be built from Cumberland, Maryland, on the Potomac, to proceed north-westerly across Pennsylvania" and connect with the Ohio River at Wheeling. A year after the committee was appointed, Congress, with remarkable speed, appropriated $30,000 "to regulate the laying out and making a road from Cumberland, in the state of Maryland, to the state of Ohio," and specifying that the road be built to high standards:

"All parts of the road which the President shall direct to be made, in case the trees are standing, shall

Near Washington, Pa., 1910.

be cleared the full width of four rods and the road shall be raised in the middle of the carriage-way with stone, earth or gravel or sand, or a combination of some or all of them, leaving or making, as the case may be, a ditch or water course on each side contiguous to said carriage-way, and in no instance shall there be an elevation in said road, when finished, greater than an angle of five degrees with the horizon, that the manner of making such road in every other particular, is left to the direction of the President."

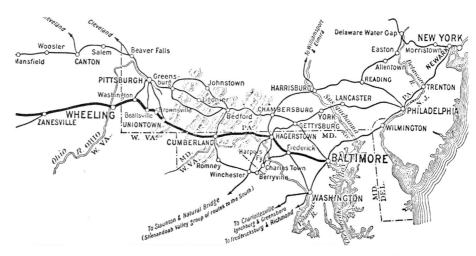

Evolution of The National Road.

Near Brownsville, Pa. (1910 photo).

Near Hancock, Md. (1920 photo).

The last phrase suggests the early origins of the standard coverall clause in modern contract documents which provides that no matter what else is prescribed, the work may be done "as the Engineer directs."

The War of 1812 delayed the start of construction on the National Road. Nevertheless, it was completed to Wheeling by 1818 and, by 1824, was already in need of heavy repair work. President Monroe signed a bill providing funds for rehabilitation and extension of the road.

At about this same time, road construction technology was undergoing a major advance. The developments were conceived by two Scots, Thomas Telford and John Louden McAdam.

Telford developed the concept of heavy stone foundations, with smaller stones for the upper layers of the road. McAdam extended Telford's ideas. McAdam recognized the load bearing capacity of soil when kept dry and compact. He said that a road with an impervious surface, along with proper crowning for drainage, would suffice to carry normal traffic.

From there, McAdam went on to develop such an impervious surface. It was

A wagon dumps stone in windrows for resurfacing a macadamized road.

composed of clean, broken stones of a fairly small, uniform size. Once such a surface was put in place, McAdam said, it would actually improve with traffic service. Traffic would not only pack the stones tightly together, but it would also lay across them a binding dust which would further increase their resistance to water penetration.

McAdam's principles remain sound. Such roads still exist. They have long been known as "macadam" roads.

John Louden McAdam.

CHAPTER 4

WATER, STEAM, MUD AND DUST

Just as one Scotsman, J.L. McAdam, provided the foundation for substantial improvement in roads, yet another Scotsman, James Watt, a contemporary of Telford and McAdam, provided what eventually would be the undoing of American roads. In 1769, he patented substantial improvements in the steam engine and worked continually toward their perfection until he retired a wealthy man in 1800. He did not, however, provide the means to put steam to use. In the late 1700's, John Fitch of Philadelphia tried three times to devise a practicable steamboat by applying the steam engine to the propulsion of a ship. His first boat on the Delaware River, a monstrosity propelled by six paddles driven on a side, like an Indian canoe, by a steam engine, was a technical disaster. In 1807, John Fulton's Claremont, sailing up the Hudson River from New York City to Albany, succeeded where Fitch had failed, in part because of Fulton's concern for passenger comfort. He had regular schedules for dinner and tea, and provided berths and creature comforts for his passengers. Comfort, speed, and economics led to substantial use of the waterways, which were more convenient and less rugged than the wilderness.

On land, travel was perilous for both passenger and freight. The freight wagon with its heavier loads and narrower wheels "turned a wide common into deeply worn bridle paths and cart tracks into far wider and deeper courses." Where one wagon had gone, leaving great black ruts behind it, another wagon would pass with greater difficulty leaving behind it yet deeper and more treacherous tracks. "Heavy

rains would fill each cavity with water, making the road nothing less than what in Illinois was known as a 'sloo'." Historian Archer B. Hulbert observed: "Such was the frightful condition of the old roads that four or five yoke of oxen conveyed only a ton of cotton so slowly that motion was almost imperceptible; and in the winter and spring, it has been said, with perhaps some tinge of truthfulness, that one could walk on dead oxen from Jackson to Vicksburg. The bull-skin road of pioneer days leading from the Pickaway Plains in Ohio to Detroit was so named from the large number of cattle which died, on the long, rough route, their hides, to exaggerate again, lining the way."

For travelers, such roads presented an adventure at least. One of the most

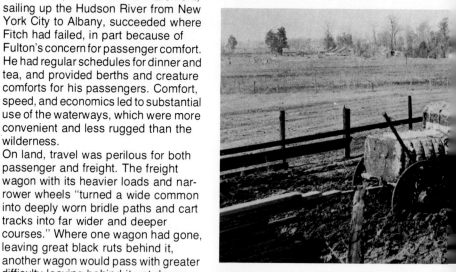

Cotton hauling in North Carolina, early 1900's.

Indiana Road about 1904, a midwestern "sloo."

graphic descriptions came from Charles Dickens in his *American Notes* published in 1830. This portion deals with an account of his travels from Washington on the Potomac to Fredericksburg, Virginia, by stagecoach:

"The coaches are something like the French coaches, but not nearly so good. In lieu of springs, they are hung on bands of the strongest leather. There is very little choice or difference between them; and they may be likened to the car portion of the swings at an English fair, roofed, put upon axle-trees and wheels, and curtained with painted canvas. They are covered with mud from the roof to the wheel-tire, and have never been cleaned since they were first built . . .

"The coach holds nine inside, having a seat across from door to door, where we

in England put our legs so that there is only one feat more difficult in the performance than getting in, and that is getting out again."

He describes the driver: "He is a Negro—very black indeed. He is dressed in a coarse pepper-and-salt suit excessively patched and darned (particularly at the knees), grey stockings, enormous unblackened high-low shoes, and very short trousers. He has two odd gloves: one a party-colored worsted, and one of leather." While he is making the notes, Dickens hears someone cry "Go ahead!" He observes: "By the way, whenever an Englishman would cry 'All Right!' an American cries 'Go ahead!' which is somewhat expressive of the national character of the two countries."

"The first half mile of the road is over bridges made of loose planks laid across two parallel poles, which tilt up as the wheels roll over them; and *in* the river. The river has a clayee bottom and is full of holes, so that half a horse is constantly disappearing unexpectedly, and can't be found again for some time.

"But we get past even this, and come to the road itself, which is a series of alternate swamps and gravel-pits. A tremendous place is close before us. The black driver rolls his eyes, screws mouth up very round, and looks straight between the two leaders as if he were saying to himself, 'We have done this often before, but *now* I think we shall have a crash!' . . . We come to the spot, sink down in the mire nearly to the coach windows, tilt on one side at an angle of 45 degrees, and stick there. The insides scream dismally; the coach stops; the horses flounder; all the other six

Washington, D.C. (Georgetown), about 1819.

North Carolina roads improved.

Chicago, 1831.

Canal at Columbia, Pa.

coaches stop; and their four-and-twenty horses flounder likewise: but merely for company, and in sympathy with ours." In 1808, Albert Gallatin, Secretary of the Treasury, presented a report that extended the case for federal involvement for road building within the states. But his comprehensive report included not only roads; it also called for an inland waterway from Massachusetts to North Carolina, east-to-west improvement of the rivers emptying into the Atlantic, construction of canals connected by turnpike roads across the Alleghenies and the development of inland navigation between the East Coast, the Great Lakes, and the St. Lawrence River.

In his *Oxford History of the American People,* Samuel Eliot Morison notes that as a result of the territories gained in the War of 1812, the impetus for implementing Gallatin's ideas was heightened as expansion to the west began more vigorously. Between 1810 and 1820 the population of states and territories west of the Appalachians more than doubled. Four new states—Indiana, Mississippi, Illinois and Alabama were

admitted to the Union. Steam traffic increased on the rivers. In 1817 a steam boat chugged up the Mississippi to Cincinnati. Two years later, 60 light-draught stern-wheelers, were steaming between New Orleans and Louisville, with freight charges to the upper Ohio Valley less than half the cost of wagon transport from Philadelphia and Baltimore. For selfish reasons, eastern cities would not promote the western desire for Federal roads and canals.

Pennsylvania built her own roads, and later her own canals, and New York in 1817 began the construction of the Erie Canal, which was destined to make New York City outstrip all rival seaports.

In 1817 also, the first railroad in the United States was built in Quincy, Mass., and shortly thereafter the Baltimore and Ohio railroad was chartered. By 1830, 23 miles of railroad were operating in the United States. Ten years later, this would be expanded to 2,800 miles of operating railroad lines, and by 1850, some 9,000 railroads would be in operation. Every group of ambitious bankers, merchants, tradesmen, and speculators

started his own small railroad, laying the foundations for the great railroad acquisition wars later in the century.

At the same time, tonnage on the canals was moving in substantial quantity. In 1837, the first year records were kept, over 1.1 million tons of cargo moved on canals in New York State alone. By 1850, cargo on the New York State water system rose to 3 million tons. The push west arose early and continued strong. The Santa Fe Trail was opened in 1825 along an unimproved route marked by two settlements and few guideposts to the southwest. The reach to the northwest opened the Oregon Trail in 1843. The persecution in Illinois of the Mormons led them into Utah in 1846. Routes to California opened in 1841. Ironically, the horse and oxen drawn wagons of the pioneers took them to found numerous small settlements along these routes, which later would become important for the vast, transcontinental push of the railroads.

By 1830, the United States population stood at 12,000,000. At the time, most of the population lived on the east coast —there were 1.4 million people in the midwest (Ohio, Indiana, Illinois, Michigan, Wisconsin), 1.8 million in the middle south (Kentucky, Tennessee, Alabama, Mississippi), and another 150,000 in the territories of Louisiana and what would become Arkansas. In the 1830's, Chicago was a town of but 350 people; yet in 1833, over 300 vessels visited the Port of Chicago. By 1856, Chicago was connected by railroad to New York; by 1860 its population well exceeded 100,000 persons. The economic effects of rail and canal transportation were enormous. Even before 1830, the governor of Georgia was complaining that wheat from central New York was being sold in Savannah more cheaply than wheat from central Georgia. At the same time, Philadelphians, who prided themselves on being the leaders of commerce and finance as well as the cradle of American government, were shocked to find it was cheaper to ship goods to Pittsburgh by New York canals than over the roads that then existed.

Broadway, New York City, about 1855.

1822 THE SANTA FÉ TRAIL

Plank road across California desert.

But during the great period of railroad growth, the canals themselves were soon to lose their economic advantage to the railroads, which received subsidies from the federal government to an extent never enjoyed by the turnpike companies or the builders of roads. With the value of the west, the need for it to absorb the incoming emigrants, the need for its wealth and riches, and the American penchant for seeking freedom of movement and expression, the railroads shortly were to be extended west. The great race began with an act of Congress of July, 1862, granting to the Union Pacific and Central Pacific Railroad companies a 200-foot right-of-way. The sale of public lands was to produce vast sums of money for the federal government and for the owners of the railroads. The railroads sold millions of acres for profit to finance their construction, and also received federal subsidies. The Union Pacific especially was favored in its building westward from Omaha until meeting the Central Pacific in 1869 in Promontory Point, Utah. The track layers, to obtain freight rights and land adjacent to the railroads, forced construction at fantastic rates. Seven miles a day of track laid became common, the record being 10 miles laid in a single day. Gangs of up to 10,000 laborers, many of them Irish or Chinese, lived for months, and indeed through the winter, in the wilderness in their race to complete the railroads.

The railroad companies assisted materially in expansion of the west by providing inexpensive rates and land sales to immigrants. The Northern Pacific railroad of James Hill, recognizing the value of the commerce from the farm lands, set a policy that it would not subsidize immigrants who lived beyond 10 miles from the railway lines. Such were the conditions of roads and transportation to the market. This recognition of the need to reach the farmer for his commerce later in the century led the railroads to become prime supporters of the demand for better roads.

Although the turnpikes provided the best-paved roads of the early eighteenth century, with their economic difficulties they rapidly began to deteriorate. In addition to those surfaced with gravel, others were "paved" with shell and others corduroyed. At the same time, many were surfaced with wood planks, an idea originating in Toronto, Ontario, Canada, about 1835, and over the next several years widely introduced in the United States. Some 2,000 miles of plank roads were built in New York State alone at an average cost of $1,833 per mile. An 1850 report describes them as follows: "They were in nearly all cases of single track, laid on the right side of the road as one faced the large town to which it led. In the prairie regions the planking lay on the original surface of the ground, but in some places a small amount of grading was needed to avoid short, steep ascents. The sub-grade once established, longitudinal trenches were dug in which sills consisting of three inch plank, four and eight inches wide, were placed, and on them were laid the planks, three inches thick and eight feet long, at right angles to the direction of the road.

"The sills were set-slightly below the surface of the ground, and the planks were pounded down to rest upon them by means of a large mallet known as a 'Commander.' No nails or pins were then needed to hold the planks down, and it is reported that it was hard work to take one of them up. After the planks were laid, the earth was packed against their ends and soundly tamped into place . . . Over the completed planking a layer of sand was spread and maintained, which preserved the road by reducing the cutting by the caulks of the horse-shoes. It was claimed for this coating that a saving of forty to fifty percent was secured in the

Leavenworth, Kansas, in the late 1800's.

wear of the road. Very few double-track roads were ever laid, and in the few cases it was preferred to lay two single tracks, apart from each other and supposedly on opposite sides of the 'turnout'."

Throughout the nation, the roads fell into disrepair and disuse. Serving now as mainly feeders for the railroad, they were described by one writer as "large clouds of dust in summer and streams of mud in winter." Maintenance fell primarily to the county courts. Each year the court appointed a surveyor within each precinct, whose duty was to notify persons who were required by law to work on the roads. One such law, in Virginia and West Virginia, required each man over 21 and under 50 years of age to work at least 2 days on the road in his precinct between April and September. Not more than 4 days work would be required in one year, it was noted, "except in cases of emergency." A West Virginia report notes that if any individual chose not to do the work, he could "pay his way out" at the rate of not less than 75 cents and no more than $1.25 for each day he was

Indiana road in 1911.

supposed to labor.

"However, those who chose to work seldom took their labor seriously," a report of the day notes. "They engaged in horseplay and often turned the meeting into a social, rather than utilitarian event. The system was, in fact, closely akin to that employed in medieval times, and Governor McCorkle characterized the system as a miserable one."

Maintenance was often carried out by individual farmers using horse-drawn drags and scarifiers—toothed harrows and other type drags used to break up the surface. The surface then would sometimes be dragged and scraped into a resemblance of a crown and smoothed over.

Meanwhile the search for better surfacing materials to rid the roads of ruts and mud was undertaken in several ways. In 1830 in Philadelphia, brick was tried as a paving material, but it did not stand in place correctly and was discontinued. A bituminous paving material was patented in 1834.

A tar aggregate combination was not totally satisfactory in that it required a

Rolled subgrade, 1914.

Drag in use, circa 1907.

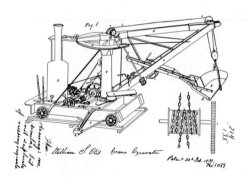

Crane design, 1809.

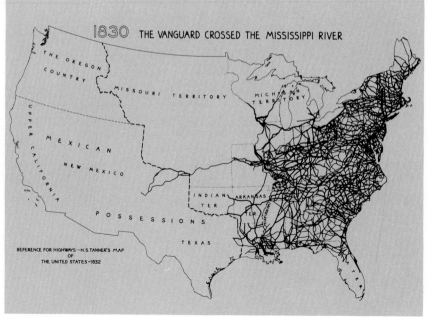

month to harden sufficiently to bear horse and carriage travel.

Power equipment, in addition to steam ships and railroad engines, was beginning to be developed about this time; in 1838, William S. Otis of Massachusetts developed the first American steam shovel for digging the road bed for the Western railroad in Massachusetts. (In the 1840's steam buses were tried but never proved popular.)

One of the more significant developments was the invention of the jaw rock crusher by Eli Whitney Blake in 1858.

While providing broken rock for the surfacing of roads, particularly by the McAdam process, may have seemed burdensome work by hand, the invention of the rock crusher was not totally welcomed. As late as 1890 one critic wrote, "Hand-broken stone is much superior to that broken by machine, which is generally of irregular shape and seldom cubicle, so that it does not readily bind together, which is the essential qualification of McAdam."

In 1859, the steam roller was invented by Lemoine and was first imported into

Brick-making machine.

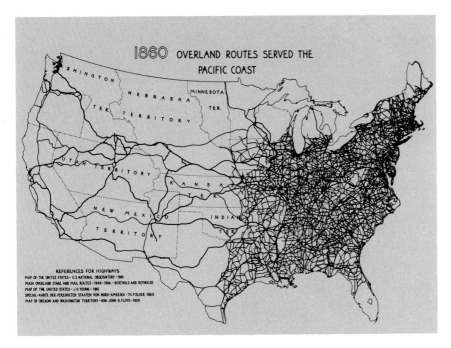

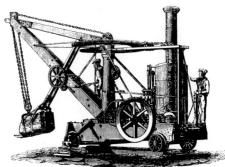

Excavator, 1845.

THE AVELING & PORTER ROLLER.

THE ROSS ROLLER.

Fig. 1

A mid-18th Century improvement, "Coxes Double-Dumping Machine."

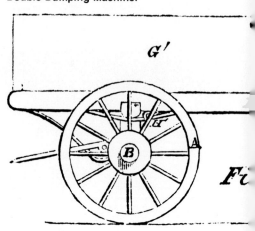

the United States ten years later. In 1872, the first brick and sheet asphalt streets were laid. In Charleston, West Virginia, brick was successfully developed for street use and arduously laid by hand. The sheet asphalt treatment took place on Pennsylvania Avenue in Washington, D.C. in 1879. Preceeding this, rock asphalt had been used in a short stretch of street in Newark, New Jersey, opposite the city hall in 1870, another short section laid in New York in 1873, and yet another in Newark in 1877.

The United States was still growing westward. In 1860, the United States total population was 31,500,000, most still in the eastern, midwestern, and southern Atlantic states, but with some 2,000,000 in the West. In 1860, the New York State canal shipped some 4.6 million tons of goods, and on the Sault Ste. Marie traffic had grown to 154,000 tons, 120,000 tons of it being iron ore. 30,000 miles of railroad track had been constructed throughout the nation before the Civil War. Over 1.1 billion dollars had been invested in railroads and railroad equipment by 1860.

The Civil War came and went with little effect against the neglect of roads caused already by the competition of canals, of rails, of a financially-pressed or rights-concerned government.

By 1880, the population of the United States had reached 50 million persons, with that part west of the Mississippi River approaching 8 million. New York State canal tonnage peaked that year at 4.6 million tons, not to be exceeded until 1936. By 1880, some 115,000 miles of railroad track was in use and railroad revenues that year were some $600 million on a total investment of $4.6 billion. Ten years later railroad investment reached $8.7 billion in road bed and equipment (out of a total capital investment of $10 billion) and the total mileage in use exceeded 166,000 miles.

Rock crusher.

Iowa brick laying, 1917. Methods remained unchanged from the 1870's. Photo information notes the man "in the white shirt could lay 500 feet of 20-foot paving in one day."

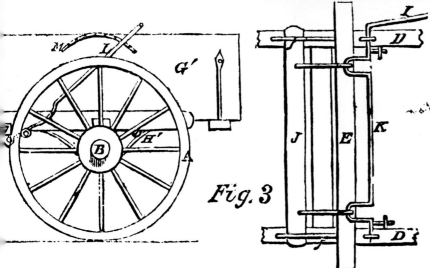

Fig. 3

CHAPTER 5

BIKES AND BYWAYS

Despite technical innovations and increasing traffic, most American roads remained in deplorable condition throughout the Nineteenth Century. As an American geologist put it in 1889, "In most rural districts of the United States the common ways are built and maintained in the most ignorant and inefficient manner. In no other phase of public duties does the American citizen appear to such disadvantage as in the construction of roads. Generally, road making and the so-called road mending are performed not by a tax of money but by an impost on the labor of the county. The voting part of the population is summoned each year to give one or two days to working out the road tax."

In terms of miles, the road system was extensive. About 2,000,000 miles of roads existed by 1890, a number equivalent to more than half of the 1975 total road mileage. But two out of three Americans lived in the rural areas, and rural America was not enthusiastic about roads.

One key reason for the reluctance of the farm population to pay for the paving of rural highways was the inability of the typical farmer to see any benefit accruing to him. According to Jeremiah W. Jenks, a persistent contemporary critic of rural road conditions, "A very large proportion of our people have never seen a really good road for hauling purposes, and have in consequence, no clear idea of the gain that would come from good roads. The result to farmers and the rural population was a constant sea of mud, soft surfaces, impediments to travel that in fact reduced their ability to communicate with their neighbors or move their goods to market."

The urban road situation was considerably better. By 1890, there were three American cities with a million or more people and 25 more with populations in excess of 100,000. While there were many unimproved streets, it was common for the main thoroughfares to be paved with stone or brick. In the larger cities, the street transportation system was supplemented by horse-drawn (later electric) trolleys. Internal transportation facilities seldom extended into the countryside. "It was a hardy soul indeed," one commentator reported, "who would venture with his wagon down the unimproved roads for a picnic, a visit to relatives, or a pleasant escape with a friend from the pressures of the city."

Transportation inadequacies contributed to a cultural gap between the city dweller and his country cousin. There was little to encourage the city man to visit the rural areas, and *vice versa*.

A straw road near Davenport, Washington.

44

Chicago, 1903. Note trolleys, stone streets.

As transportation historian John N. Rae notes, "Before serious attention could be given to the highway situation, something had to come along to get people out on the roads in large numbers and create an awareness of flexibility and convenience of travel by road." In the 1880's, "something" did come along. It was the bicycle.

The first bicycles, walking models, had been developed in Europe around 1790. The high-wheeled bicycle, with pedals on the big front wheel, was introduced into the United States at the Philadelphia Centennial Exposition in 1876. It was relatively comfortable, but difficult to mount and dangerous to operate. In spite of its disadvantages, the high-wheeler quickly became popular. Its riders formed a national organization which was to have a significant impact on road development, the League of

American Wheelmen.

The bicycle boom, and the League, really began to move ahead with the introduction into this country of the "safety bicycle" about the middle of the 1880's. The "safety bicycle," with a configuration much like the modern machine, was easy to ride.

Furthermore, the price was right. The early bicycles were quite expensive, costing $150 to $200. At its beginning, 60 percent of the members of the League of American Wheelmen came from the affluent states of New York and Massachusetts. With quantity production, the price of bicycles came down to about $30. By the mid-1890's, there were 4,000,000 regular bicycle riders in the United States. In 1899, there were 312 factories manufacturing 1,000,000 bicycles a year.

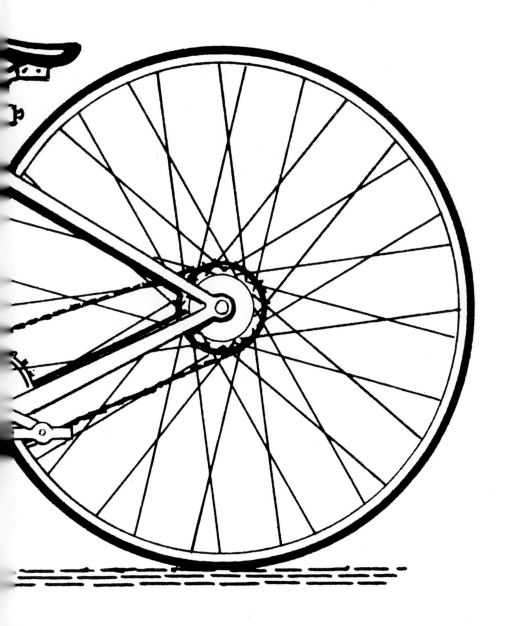

Westminister, Md. street before improvement . . .

In pressing for improved roads, the cyclists found allies among two influential, albeit unlikely groups—the railroads and the farmers.

The Populists, headed by the silver-tongued William Jennings Bryan, attacked the "public be damned" attitude of the large railroads, and probably influenced a more public spirited attitude. More importantly, the railroads gradually saw the advantages of improved roads in the farm regions. These advantages were both general and specific. Generally, roads would improve regional economies and enhance the railroads' market potential. Specifically, all-weather roads from farm to railhead would make farmers less dependent on good weather for moving their crops and thus spread out traffic throughout the year.

As for the farmers, they were inclined to favor anything that would ease their economic dependence on the railroads. They had to be persuaded, however, that the "good roads" movement would amount to more than an excuse to place new tax burdens on the farmer.

The National Grange played an important part in mustering farm support for highways. With support from the Grange and other key farm organizations, the National League for Good Roads was founded in 1892. One year later, the League held its first Good Roads Convention, in Washington, D.C.

That same year, the Office of Road Inquiry, was created. Significantly, it was an agency of the Department of Agriculture. General Roy Stone, a long-time advocate of road improvement, was appointed to head the Office. Congress gave him a budget of $10,000 to conduct tests and experiments on roadbuilding material and to disseminate information on road improvements through agricultural colleges and experiment stations. Significant action also took place on the state level. While Kentucky had had a state highway department from 1821 to 1837, responsible for building 340 miles or road, there was little other evidence of state interest in roads until 1891, when New Jersey's legislature passed an act enabling the state to participate directly in road construction. Massachusetts took similar action in 1892; California and Connecticut in 1895; Maryland, New York and Vermont in 1898. By 1910, 26 states had established highway construction responsibilities.

The Federal interest in roads was greatly augmented by Congressional

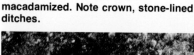

... **and street in same town macadamized. Note crown, stone-lined ditches.**

authorization, in 1893, of Rural Free Delivery. This mail service was made contigent on the existence of an improved —that is, gravel or macadam—road. RFD service was initiated around Charleston, West Virginia, in 1896 and was operative nationally within four years. This led to demands for Federal assistance for road improvements. In 1913, the Post Office Appropriations Act made $500,000 available to 17 states which elected to cooperate in the program. This money, along with $1,300,000 of state and local funds, built 425 miles of road.

Postal service was important, but basic economics remained the key. William Jennings Bryan told the Good Roads Convention of 1903: "The improvement of the country roads can also be justified on the ground that the farmer, first and most important of the producers of wealth, ought to be in a position to hold his crop and market it at the most favorable opportunity, whereas at present he is virtually under compulsion to sell it as soon as it is matured, because the roads may become impassable at any time during the fall, winter or spring." (He went on to cite the advantages to education, morality, fellowship, and many other benefits to the farmer from the improvement of roads. Rural life was perhaps revered more in those days by the politicians than by those who lived on the farms.)

Mecklenburg County, North Carolina, began in 1880 to macadamize three or four miles of road a year at an expenditure of about $10,000. Historian A.B. Hulbert, noting that the county "now (1904) has over 100 miles of splendid roads", reported that "land that had cost ten dollars an acre now was refused for sale at forty-six dollars an acre" and "yet not a dollar has been put on it, not even to fertilize it. Some of the farms five and six miles from town have quadrupled in value."

The Office of Road Inquiry, in 1895, attempted to determine the total tonnage and costs of hauling on the public roads. General Stone's office computed the average load as being "two pounds over a ton" and the average cost at 25 cents per ton mile. Stone estimated that two-thirds of the cost of transportation could be saved by road improvements which would reduce the wear and tear on draft animals, permit heavier loads to be hauled and reduce travel time.

Economic analysis was important, but the greatest and most lasting contribution of the Office of Road Inquiry was the establishment of research procedures. These were to be urgently needed within a few years, with the advent of the motor-powered highway vehicle and greatly increased demands on the highway system.

1900 photo shows object lesson road, of brick and limestone surface, being rolled.

Martin Dodge, who succeeded Stone at the Office of Road Inquiry in 1898, began a program of building "object-lesson roads" to demonstrate the value of good roads and provide local authorities with roadbuilding experience. In 1900, Dodge and his engineers laid out "object-lesson roads" near Port Huron, Saginaw and Traverse City, Michigan; Springfield, Illinois, and Topeka, Kansas. The next year, roads were built as object lessons in Louisiana, Mississippi, Tennessee, Kentucky, Illinois, New York, North Carolina, South Carolina, Alabama and Georgia.

Those were the days of the "good roads trains." The typical train, of either the Illinois Central or the Southern Railway, included two carloads of officials and road experts and ten carloads of roadbuilding machinery. Both the experts and the machines were unloaded at stops along the way to demonstrate advanced techniques and to promote subsequent sales.

In 1904, the Office of Road Inquiry made the first complete census of American roads. It found only 153,000 miles of surfaced roads in the rural areas, including 114,899 miles with gravel, sand-

clay, shell, plank and other "low-type" surfaces. There were 38,622 miles of water-bound macadam, and exactly 141 miles with surfaces "better than macadam." These top-drawer roads included 123 miles of rural brick roads in Ohio and West Virginia, and 18 miles paved with bituminous materials—16 miles in Ohio and two in Massachusetts. The census also counted 2,500 miles of oiled earth roads in California.

Quite appropriately, the Office of Road Inquiry's advice dealt extensively with earth roads, recognizing that earth is "the poorest material for road construction, except for sand, that is known." It advised that longitudinal grades be kept to one foot in thirty, with a one to twenty slope from crown to side. "The great enemy of roads is water." To make the surface smooth and compact, it should be "rolled and re-rolled a number of times."

However, before rolling, the road should be "harrowed or scarified. In level countries and with narrow roads, enough material may be excavated to raise the roadway above the subgrade in forming the side ditches." These side ditches were created by the use of grading machines, the blade set at any desired

1913 photo of old and new earth-graded roads, Wise County, Va.

angle, which, when drawn along by horses, "cuts into the surface and moves the earth from the sides toward the center, forming gutters alongside and distributing the earth uniformly over the traveled way."

The Office of Road Inquiry was a stalwart advocate of mechanization. "The labor-saving machinery now manufac-

tured for road building is just as effectual and necessary as the modern mower, self-binder and thresher. Road graders and rollers are the modern inventions necessary to permanent and economical construction. Two men with two teams can build more road in a day with a grader and roller than 50 men can with picks and shovels, and do it more uniformly and more thoroughly."

Paving with marble, Tennessee, 1911.

Gravel roads were to be preferred over earth roads, and a hard-surfaced road was better yet. "On a well-made gravel road one horse can pull twice as large a load as he can on a well-made earth road. On a hard, smooth stone road, one horse can pull as much as four horses will on a good earth road."

Gravel was usually carried in dump carts and wheelbarrows, and then spread in even layers "with rakes, but the latest

and best device for this purpose is the spreading cart." The road then could be rolled by traffic "but the work may be hastened and facilitated by the use of a horse roller or light steam roller . . . and better results accomplished by this means."

As for macadamized roads, much to be preferred for their hard surface, "modern machinery and screens can provide perfectly adequate stones. A good crusher driven by eight horsepower will turn out from 40 to 80 cubic yards of two-inch stone per day of ten hours, and will cost from $400 upward," according to an engineer of the period. This surfacing was still the standard, considered to be the most economical and best for a traffic stream that consisted mainly of horse-drawn vehicles and bicycles. Properly built, the macadamized road was impervious to rain and so smooth and hard on the surface that "the horses' hoofs would ring upon it."

The successful macadam road, the experts said, depended on two related elements—proper grading and the correct size and type of stone. The stone, "broken to pass a two-inch ring," would compact solidly under rolling and use. Minimal maintenance was recommended for macadamized roads, except that stone roads had to be scraped to remove dust and mud. For this, hand scraping with a hoe was considered best because "machinery, no matter how carefully adjusted, is liable to ravel a road by loosening some of the stones." To rebuild these roads, it was necessary to break the bond of the surface before placing a new layer "either by picking it up by hand or by a steam roller with short spikes in its surface."

The Office of Road Inquiry was not devoid of environmental concerns. Roadside areas, it said, should be clean, not only to help drain water, but also to provide walkways for pedestrians. Trees should be planted, but "far enough back to admit the wind and the sun."

Money was a problem, of course. However, the Office of Road Inquiry noted that "the introduction in recent years of improved road-building machinery has enabled the authorities in some of the states to build improved stone and gravel roads quite cheaply." In New York, for example, "first class, single track stone roads, nine feet wide" were constructed for $900 to $1,000 per mile. Macadam roads cost $2,000 to $5,000 per mile.

CHAPTER

ROAD "MAKERS" AND ROAD "BUILDERS"

At the turn of the century, the instructions of the Office of Road Inquiry and other documents spoke of "making" roads. In the next few years, the language changed. Roads were not "made," they were "built." The change in terminology is significant. It reflects the recognition that the motor vehicle brought with it the necessity for a new road technology.

By 1902, the base of support for better roads had widened well beyond the interests of the League of American Wheelmen. The leadership of the Wheelmen was instrumental in the organization of the American Road Makers in 1902. In 1910, the American Road Makers changed its name to the American Road Builders' Association. ARBA and the American Good Roads Congress met jointly in Rochester, New York, in 1911. Approximately 1,400 delegates from the United States and Canada attended the meeting, viewed exhibits of machinery and materials, and discussed technical aspects of road building.

There were already 500,000 motor vehicles registered in the United States. It was a time of transition. It was clear that the automobile would become an increasingly important transportation vehicle. Some of the delegates, at least, saw a need for better pavement types and better roadbuilding techniques. There was recognition of a need for trunk lines, connected systems and improved maintenance. However, many of the roadbuilders were still primarily concerned with horse-and-wagon transportation. They repeated many complaints about farmers' roads "so slippery that horses cannot keep their footing."

One who recognized that the times were changing was Nelson P. Lewis, the chief

64

10-ton steam roller exhibited at 1909
Road Show.

Texaco sheet asphalt being applied in Florida. 1917 photo.

Granite block repair in New York City.

engineer of New York City. "Within the last decade," he said, "has appeared the high speed road locomotive, or automobile, and it soon became apparent that, while water bound stone roads stood up fairly well under rolling loads, they were not calculated to resist the action of driving wheels, and it is now universally recognized that a different kind of building material must be used." He recommended bituminous macadam for consideration because "the commercial use of such vehicles (automobiles), which is just beginning in this country, both as to the number of vehicles and their carrying capacity, will doubtless increase very rapidly . . . a consideration which . . . should govern the type of road to be constructed." He said the materials that could be used included broken stone and bituminous binder, stone blocks bound with concrete, and sheet or monolithic concrete. Following Lewis' discussion, a Mr. Lyon (the transcript does not fully identify all participants) of New York responded: "You may talk about the kind, quality and class of material to be used in the construction of highways all you want to, but I want to say that there are three great propositions in this question of highway improvement, and the first is drainage! the second is drainage! and the third is drainage! (Applause)." Some, concerned with the need for new technology, emphasized the need for

engineers. Others, perhaps feeling that a basic understanding of drainage would solve all problems, disagreed. The motor vehicle created roadbuilding problems, but might also help solve some. Mr. McClintock of Monroe County, New York, discussed the use of "the power truck in the maintenance of roads," commenting that the use of a man and a team is, by contrast, "the most expensive kind of work that can be done." Based on his personal experience, he said gravel could be hauled, three tons at a time, for a 38-mile distance, a job which "could not have been done with four or five teams in the same time."

The hot-mix asphalt plant was still to be developed, but people were racking their brains for ideas. "It occurred to me about two years ago," said a Mr. Ruggles, "that if asphalt could be pulverized and shipped to the work in bags, it would be possible to heat the stone, mix the pulverized asphalt with it, and get the same results as if the asphalt were heated on the ground."

Mr. Dingman of Wayne County (Detroit), Michigan, said that "concrete, in my mind," would withstand the greatest travel of vehicles of any description that might come upon them." A concrete pavement had been laid three years earlier, on Woodward Avenue. "I don't believe $100 has been spent for repairs," he said. The initial cost was reported to

1920's photo of first Portland cement concrete street, Woodward Avenue, Wayne County, Michigan, laid in 1908.

be $12,000 to $16,000 a mile. These costs might be considered high in some bailiwicks, but Detroit was beginning to ride high. A Wayne County colleague said the population was 500,000 and the automobile industry payroll was $30,000,000 a year. The county had 302 miles of paved or improved road, "largely for the automobile; we have the money and can afford it." Outside of Wayne County, gravel roads were being built at an average cost of $1,638 a mile, macadam roads at $4,250.

Costs varied widely, depending on quality. From the state of Washington, Mr. Roberts reported road costs ranging from eight dollars a mile for "converting a sandy road into an automobile speedway by means of a split log drag" to as much as $10,000 to $15,000 a mile for hard-surfaced city streets. Others reported various combinations of asphalt and oil treatment costing between $2,500 and $3,500 a mile, "depending on the kind of method you use with your oil and sand."

Brooming oil over roadway, 1911.

Paving in El Dorado County, California, 1917.

Cold application of "Trinidad tar."

It was the beginning of a time of rapid expansion. In 1910, Portland cement concrete was used to pave about 20 miles of road, the next year 40 miles, in

1912, 250 miles more. By 1914, the total
was 2,348 miles. Brick paving was in its
heyday. In 1914, 1,600 miles of brick
paving existed; by 1924, this had been

Laying block pavement in Washington, D.C. 1917.

increased to 4,319 miles. The amount of bituminous concrete on rural roads was negligible in 1914, but in 1924 there were 9,700 miles of rural bituminous surfacing.

Numerous mixtures were tried to improve the durability of roads, eliminate dust and reduce travel noise. A "road mix" of light oil and desert sand was tried by the county engineer of San Bernardino County, California, in 1915, who used plows and harrows to develop the blend. Various types of asphaltic concrete, mixing hot mineral aggregates with hot asphalt, were tried, following a patent issued to F.J. Warren in 1903. The "Topeka mix" originated in 1910. The use of mechanical spreaders for bituminous concrete was not developed until about 1928.

Underlying the growth of activity were two concurrent but diverse influences: the advent and development of the automobile, and the increasing role of Federal government assistance to the states in their financing of highway construction.

CHAPTER 7

CARS CHANGE AMERICA

Better roads were, indeed, needed. The growth of automobile traffic exceeded all predictions.

The original ideas for motor vehicles evolved in Europe, where Gottleib Daimler, in 1884, patented the first commercially successful gasoline driven motor car. Eight years later, Dr. Rudolph Diesel patented an oil-powered expulsion type engine, significant to the highway construction industry in that it later proved to be the most efficient power source for earth-moving and roadbuilding machinery, as well as highway trucks and railroad trains.

Charles Duryea built the first American gasoline driven motor vehicle in 1893, and Henry Ford put together his first car in 1894. Ten years later, the Ford Motor Company had produced 1,695 cars. According to Charles E. Sorenson, Henry Ford's chief engineer, the Model T Ford

Duryea's first car, 1893.

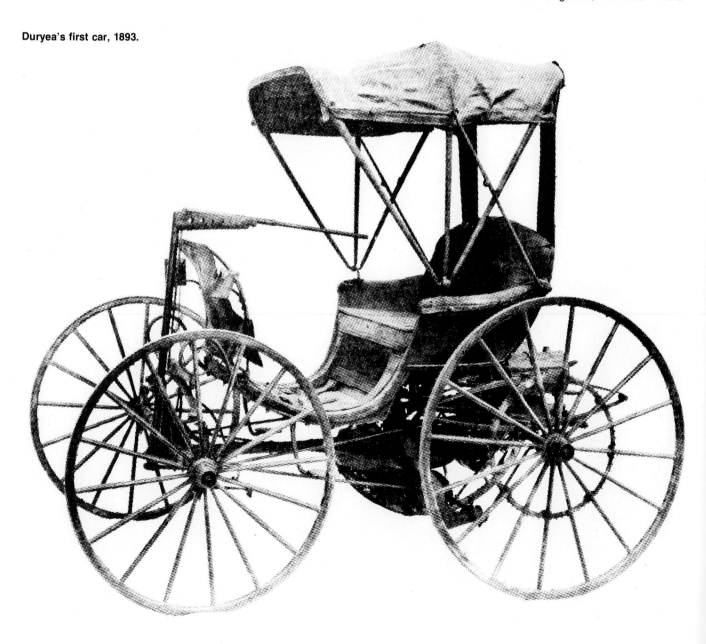

had its inception on a winter morning in 1906. Sorenson said Ford led him into a loft of the plant where experiments were made with various types of steel and that "it was primarily these new types of steel that would determine what the Model T would look like. Every day it became more evident that soon Mr. Ford would come up with something revolutionary." They took many experimental drives as the Model T evolved. "We worked through the whole year of 1907 on these problems," Sorenson noted. "By early 1908, we had built several test cars which we tried out on the roads. I did a lot of driving myself . . . Most of the roads were terrible, which was one reason why we took them; a car which survived them met the acid test. There is no better comparison of highways then and now than today's elaborate proving grounds . . . that cost the companies millions of dollars to produce synthetic hazards

that, back in 1908, we got for free. "On October 1 (1908) the first (Model T) car was introduced to the public . . . In the next 18 years, out of assembly plants all over the United States came 15 million more."

When the Model T was introduced, there was no rugged, all-purpose car selling for less than $1,500. Ford did much better than that, with two revolutionary innovations. He paid production workers $5 a day, then considered unrealistically high by most industry leaders, and he introduced the assembly line. Sorenson maintained that the assembly line was his idea. "The idea occurred to me that assembly would be easier, cheaper and faster if we moved the chassis along, beginning at one end of the plant with a frame and adding axles and wheels; then moving it past the stock room instead of moving the stock room to the chassis."

Model T assembly line.

As the assembly line improved and production increased, the price of the Model T dropped steadily, from $825 in 1908 to a low of $260 in 1925. With the automobile within reach of the working man, vehicle registrations swelled to nearly 23,000,000 in 1930. For the first time since the Civil War, cotton was displaced as the leading American export. The new leader in the export market was the automobile.

The increase in traffic volume was largely, but not entirely, responsible for the increased wear and tear on the roads. For example, the type of tire used has a substantial relationship to road wear. The early tires were derived from bicycle tires—very narrow and high pressured. Tires on the early cars were commonly inflated to pressures of 75 pounds per square inch. The use of these tires produced a hard ride and heavy roadway wear. Macadam roads proved unsuitable for the effect of the

rear-axle driving wheels and the draft created by movement at high (20 to 40 miles an hour) speed. The draft would weaken the macadam surface, breaking the bond and permitting water seepage. Truck wear was even worse. Truck use rose substantially during World War I. In 1920, the Department of Agriculture found the cost of wagon carriage to be 33 cents a ton, while truck costs were only 15 cents.

The early truck tires were of solid rubber.

Pneumatic truck tires were not generally accepted until the 1920's. Paul W. Litchfield, president of Goodyear Tire and Rubber, vigorously promoted the development of pneumatic tires for trucks. Competitor Harvey Firestone was similarly determined, in the face of considerable discouragement, to provide a pneumatic tire for off-the-road equipment. Firestone succeeded in introducing such a large, low pressure pneumatic tire about 1930.

Racing day.

Pioneer earthmover R.G. LeTourneau later observed that the development of adequate pneumatic tires was primarily responsible for the subsequent great increase in the size, capacity and power of earth-moving and construction equipment. "We always had the horsepower. What we needed was something to carry the load."

Good speed over short distances was an early attribute of the automobile. Longer distances proved a more difficult challenge, partly due to the poor state of the roads. Racing was popular from the earliest days. In 1895, J. Frank Duryea won a race between Chicago and Evanston, Illinois, at an average speed of 7½ miles an hour. Only 11 years later, a world speed record of 127.66 miles an hour was established by a Stanley Steamer. Unofficially, it hit 197 miles an hour a year later.

Long-distance travel attested to the stamina of car and driver and the deplorable state of the roads. Dr. H. Nelson

H. Nelson Jackson in Wyoming.

The scene today.

Jackson of Burlington, Vermont, traveled from San Francisco to New York by automobile in 1903. The trip required 63 days, including 44 days of running time. In 1911, a four-cylinder, 37-horsepower truck, the "Pioneer Freighter," traveled heavily loaded from New York to Los Angeles.

In 1919, Lt. Col. Dwight D. Eisenhower led an Army convoy of cars and trucks from Washington, D.C., to San Francisco to determine the adaptability of Army equipment, provide training for its drivers and "to demonstrate the necessity for the judicious expenditure of Federal government appropriations in providing for the necessary highways." The journey required 60 days.

The social effects of increasing automobile use and improved highways were nothing short of revolutionary. Cars and improved roads permitted workers with jobs in towns and cities to live miles from the jobs and to drive into the country for relaxation.

Historian Samuel Eliot Morison credits the motor vehicle, along with gasoline driven farm equipment with "emancipating the western wheat farmer from his land." He notes that filling stations and service garages sprang up along the main roads, "enterprising farm wives established country restaurants to cater to 'joy riders,' and small-time entrepreneurs set up dance halls for playboys and their pickups'."

"But none of these things were possible without good roads," Morison contin-ues. "Prior to World War I, at least nine out of ten car owners in the northern states 'put up' their cars in winter and went back to horse or steam transportation." On dirt roads "the motorist had to wear linen duster, goggles and veil for protection from the clouds of dust that every car raised. As late as 1920, an official of Jackson County, Missouri, named Harry Truman, when making his rounds, had to ballast the rear of his Dodge with concrete blocks to avoid being capsized in the potholes. But by

1925, when more than half of the families, in the north at least, either owned a car or were about to buy one on the installment plan, appropriations for hard-top roads began to pour freely out of the state legislatures."

Beginning in the 1920's, car ownership substantially changed family living patterns, economics, labor and leisure. As described by social scientists Robert S. Lynd and Howard M. Lynd in their book, *Middletown:*

"We'd rather do without clothes than give up the car," said one mother of nine children. "We used to go to his sister's to visit, but by the time we get the children shoed and dressed there wasn't any money left for car fare. Now no matter how they look we just poke 'em in the car and take 'em along." The Lynds also noted that 21 of the 26 families in their survey who owned cars did not own bathtubs: "Here we obviously have a new habit cutting in ahead of an older one and slowing down the diffusion of the latter."

Also beginning to be felt were the effects of advertising, an industry that began to grow early in the century with the selling of patent medicines and cereal. "They pound away at the Middletown people to buy cars," the Lynds observed. While some families felt the automobile helped hold the family together, others thought the opposite. "Our daughters (18 and 15) don't use our car much because they are always with somebody else in their car when we go out motoring," one business class mother lamented. The automobile was blamed for leading the younger people away from family gatherings in the evening, by the local newspaper for an increase in sex crimes, by Middletown ministers for interference with long-established religious habits. Except for the disruptions caused by wars, the Lynds concluded, "Never perhaps since the days of the campmeeting have the citizens of this community been subjected to such a powerfully focused stream of habit diffusion . . ."

CHAPTER

8

"GOOD ROADS" EARNESTLY: MONEY AND MACHINES

The pressures placed on society by the outpouring of motor vehicles were not alone sufficient to produce the boom in roadbuilding that was to take place in the 1920's and 1930's. Equipment and techniques had to be developed, and the money had to be found to pay for road improvements.

After the halting start provided by the Post Office Appropriations Act of 1912, Congress gradually brought the Federal government into the main stream of roadbuilding.

A joint Congressional committee reported in 1915 that continued and extended Federal financial aid to the states for "good roads" would indeed be constitutional. Congress not only had the responsibility to establish post roads and regulate commerce, but also to provide for the common defense and promote the general welfare. All of these broad requirements could be met, in part, by a program of road improvement assistance.

The 1915 committee did not propose a definite plan for Federal aid, but it did stimulate debate as to whether Federal grants should go directly to counties, then primarily responsible for road construction and maintenance, or whether a Federal-*state* aid system should be established. The latter view prevailed and set the pattern followed to this day.

The joint committee's report was instrumental in the enactment of the Federal Aid Road Act of 1916. The Act was extraordinarily broad in its coverage. Any rural road was eligible for Federal assistance provided only that it was, or was intended to be, used for carrying the mail. This would include, of course, almost every rural road in the nation. On the other hand, Congress took no responsibility at all for the improvement of urban streets.

The 1916 Act required that the states match Federal funds, dollar for dollar. Funds were apportioned on the basis of area, population and miles of post roads, a formula which, with modifications, still serves as the basis for the distribution of rural highway funds.

The Act emphasized the role of the states. To receive aid, they had to have state highway departments suitably organized and equipped to carry out the program. Under this plan, the Federal government left the initiative for route location decisions and standards with the states, but the states had to be able to show that their engineering organizations were competent. As a clincher, Congress made the financial assistance contigent on passing a Federal inspection at the conclusion of a project.

Along with these initiatives, the 1916 Act had some weaknesses. Although Congress looked toward the upgrading of a vast mileage of rural roads, it appropriated only $75,000,000, to be expended over a five-year period. There was no provision that any mile of Federally aided road had to be associated with any other. Thus there was no assurance that the resulting road improvements would be in any way coordinated. Another weakness: There was no enforceable requirement that the states

An "improved tractor" design, 1895.

maintain the roads properly.

With five years of learning and experience as a guide, Congress in 1921 passed a road act which was to provide the basic framework of Federal aid for many years to come. Sen. Carl Hayden of Arizona did not overstate the case when he said, in 1944, that it was an act "so sound in its fundamental provisions that it has remained for nearly a quarter of a century the basic law governing the Federal-aid highway program."

A key provision of the 1921 Act was the "seven percent" clause, which called upon state highway departments to designate a connected system of main rural roads—limited to seven percent of all rural roads in the state—as those eligible for Federal assistance. This was the first move toward a national integrated road system. The 1921 Act also made it clear that states were responsible for maintaining Federal-aid roads in perpetuity. The 1921 Act authorized $75,000,000 for the first year. Through the next 11 years, Congress would make available nearly $900 million more for road construction and improvement. As these Federal funds had to be

matched dollar-for-dollar by the states, the 1921 Act was an impetus for the states to look for a dependable source of highway funds. State taxation of gasoline began in 1923. Thus, tax revenue was closely associated with road use. This close relationship was manifested in the policy of "stage development," often called "stage construction," which was central to the idea of a self-financing road program. In developing program priorities, first attention was given to the most heavily traveled roads. Not only did these deserve priority from the standpoint of traffic service, but also these were the roads which, logically, would produce the most highway-user tax revenue.

In this "stage development" process, a road typically would be improved to its intended design standard over a period of years, new projects being authorized as funds became available. However, all of the improvements were made in accordance with the final design specifications.

Protection against water penetration was still the key to good roadbuilding practice. The fundamental principles

developed by John Louden McAdam and taught by the Office of Road Inquiry remained sound.

Macadamized roads were still used, but increasingly were protected by bituminous compounds to prevent the deterioration of their surface by vehicle vacuums and the vertical and lateral forces applied by automobile tires. However, the roads designed for heavier traffic loads generally were paved with bituminous or Portland cement concrete.

As traffic loads increased and paving technology became more sophisticated, it became more important for engineers to have an understanding of soil mechanics. Tests initiated in 1919 provided essential data on the load-bearing capacity of soils. They showed that compacting the earth, at optimum moisture levels, would vastly increase the load-bearing strength of roads. With adequate subsurface compaction, pavements could be made less thick. Technological improvements came rapidly, both in subsurface treatment and in paving. As the importance of subsurface preparation became better understood, new tools and techniques were introduced. The subsurface, or sheep's foot, roller was one device de-

Tractor and elevating grader loading horse-drawn wagon, 1920.

veloped to improve soil compaction. The results, in the early 1920's, were tentative reachings. "Stage development" was underway, which meant that there were road segments here and there constructed to high standards, while many rutted and twisted roads were still in use. Much road work was still a horse-drag and team operation, but steam had been important for some decades, and gasoline-powered equipment was not unknown. The beginnings of modern highway technology were evident, but the more primitive tools and techniques were still in common use.

Although steam-powered equipment had been used since the 1880's, the huge and heavy steam machines had the major disadvantage of becoming bogged down in loose soil, such as the soft bottom lands of California. There, in 1904, Ben Holt produced the first working crawler. It was not a new idea. Treads had been suggested since the early 1800's. Holt's contraption was not graceful. However, it worked! The Caterpillar Tractor Co. was to emerge from Holt's success.

Holt's first treaded tractor.

However, the idea of the crawler vehicle was not widely accepted until after World War I. The military "tank" demonstrated the potential of the crawler tread. By 1925, there were a half-million crawlers in the United States, mostly farm tractors.

Earth-moving involved a variety of tools, ranging from men with shovels and

Holt tractor pulling Fresno scraper. In the background, five horses pull another Fresno.

wheelbarrows, through horses and wagons, to the steam shovel. Scraping was still much a horse-drag operation. In the 1800's, a strong man with a shovel could load 12½ cubic yards of soil a day. In 1885, in Fresno, California, a blacksmith created the "Fresno scraper," a device curved and sided and reinforced so that, drawn by mules, it could move up to 100 cubic yards a day (at a cost, in 1927, of about 50 cents a yard). In the 1920's, Fresnos were commonly pulled by tractors, substantially increasing their efficiency. However, production capacity was limited and construction equipment advertising was in its infancy. The Fresno, in spite of its success, was principally marketed in the west. By the time it became known in the east, the motorized grader had appeared.

On what is now U.S. 1, near Brunswick, Maine, about 1915.

Adams motor grader.

The ancestor of the motor grader was the Adams leaning wheel grader, dating from 1885. Originally drawn by horses or steam tractors, the leaning wheel grader made grading and ditching considerably easier. However, hand shovels and wagons were still used in grading well into, and even beyond, the 'teens. Self-powered scrapers became available in the early 1920's. However, many tractor-drawn scrapers were working roads well into the 1930's. Even such maintenance equipment as snow scrapers were towed by other vehicles.

Avery gasoline-powered wheel tractor pulling hand-operated road graders.

Cutting slopes in Nebraska, 1932.

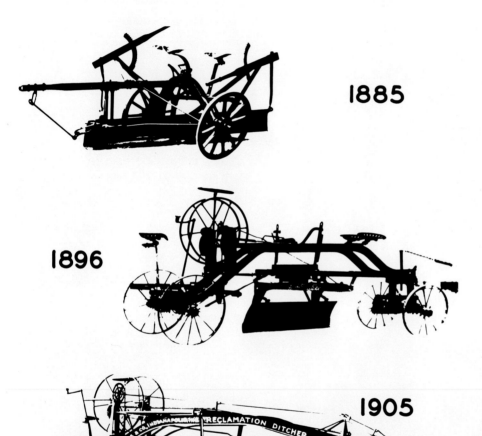

1885

1896

1905

Snow scraping in Oregon, early 1920's.

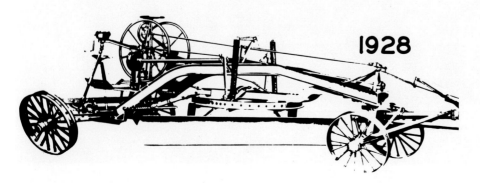

1928

96

New welding techniques came into use in World War I. R.G. LeTourneau produced his first all-welded scraper in 1922. The machine was designed to be drawn by a tractor, but it was not motorless. Electric motors tilted the six-cubic yard bowl for loading and unloading. In 1933, LeTourneau devised a scraper with a cable-operated apron which enabled it to lift the bowl and carry the load. In 1938, LeTourneau added the self-powered, single-axle tractor and

First self-propelled, electric controlled scraper, 1923.

First rubber-tired scraper.

single-axle trailer, mounted on huge
rubber tires and using hydraulic cylin-
ders for positioning the moving parts of
the scraper. The weight of the scraper
kept the nose of the tractor off the
ground, and the machine could travel at
15 mph. "This single development
probably changed the face of the
earth-moving industry more than any
other single innovation," a competitor
later noted.

**LeTourneau's six-yard "mountain
mover," 1920.**

Caterpillar was the industry leader in the development of diesel power in the 1930's, reportedly at a research and development cost of $1,000,000. With increased power, pneumatic tires, better metal fabrication and welded construction, earth-moving productivity increased. Costs of moving a cubic yard of earth dropped from 40 cents a cubic yard in 1922 to 32 cents in 1929 and 21 cents in 1938.

The age of steam was on its way out. At the 1930 Road Show (the forerunner of Conexpo), there was, for the first time, no steam shovel on display. However, steam shovels were still being used in the next decade.

The 1930 Road Show in Atlantic City.

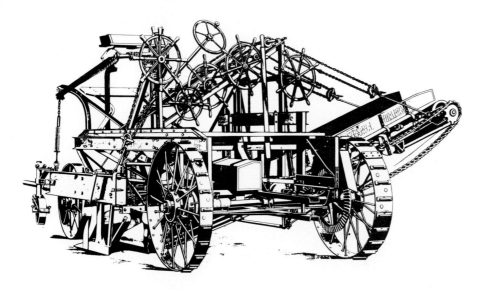

The elevating grader, pulled by a tractor and touted as "that most economical of all earth-moving machines," appeared in the 1920's. The dump truck had originated in 1905 and was used increasingly after World War I. In the 1930's, Euclid pioneered in the development of four-wheeled tractors and bottom-dump wagons.

"Fastest dirt-digger of the "twenties," the elevating scraper.

Canals, aquaducts and railroads all utilized the science of bridge building. While many highway bridges existed (mainly wooden or iron-trestled or iron-arched), ferries remained in rather common use. With the introduction into the United States of steel-reinforced concrete, again following World War I, bridge construction entered a new era and provided highway designers with a new flexibility.

Snake River ferry near Twin Falls, Idaho.

Pouring piers for the Kowaliga Bridge, 1926. The bridge crosses an Alabama Power Company impoundment.

The principle of the suspension bridge is an ancient one, but the construction of long-span successful suspension bridges had to await the development of adequate materials and the solution of complex engineering problems. In the mid-Nineteenth Century, a rivalry developed between two Pennsylvanians, the native-born Charles Ellet and the German immigrant John Augustus Roebling. Ellet's star rose and fell with the construction of a highway suspension bridge over the Ohio River at Wheeling, West Virginia, in 1849. The bridge, with a center span of 1010 feet, was the marvel of its day and Ellet went on to begin the construction of a bridge over the Niagara River Gorge. Ellet completed a light pedestrian bridge over the Niagara, but withdrew before completing the planned vehicular bridge. The Wheeling Bridge collapsed in 1854, and Roebling came into the limelight,

spanning both the Niagara and the Ohio. Roebling's crowning achievement was the famed Brooklyn Bridge, completed in 1883.

The Eads Bridge, spanning the Mississippi at St. Louis, is a remarkable engineering achievement. A triple-arch design, completed in 1874, it was the world's first steel bridge, and, in the excavation for its massive piers and abutments, it involved the first significant use of compressed air in America. The orthodox way to build an arch is to construct it over timber falsework. Eads could not obstruct the Mississippi during construction. Accordingly, the arches were cantilevered outward from the piers, the thrust balanced by falsework built above the piers.

These engineering marvels established the challenge for the great bridges of the Twentieth Century. New York's George Washington Bridge, 3500 feet from

The Holland Tunnel

tower to tower, doubled the record span length in one leap, when it was completed in 1931. In San Francisco, the Golden Gate and the Oakland-Bay bridges were both commenced in 1933.

The Golden Gate, with a 4200 foot span, was the longest in the world until the completion of the Verrazano-Narrows Bridge (4260 feet) in 1963.

On a less gargantuan scale, reinforced concrete permitted larger piers and esthetic design of other bridges, such as the Kowaliga Bridge in Alabama.

Traffic demanded tunnels, too, the first significant one for automobile traffic being New York's Holland Tunnel, completed in 1926. (The Oakland-Bay crossing, a twin suspension design with both bridges sharing a common anchorage on Yerba Buena Island, required the drilling of a half-mile highway tunnel through solid rock on the island.)

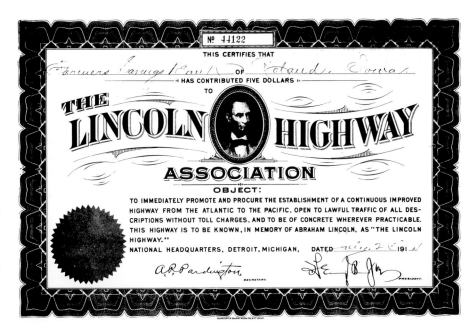

The first transcontinental highway was suggested in 1912 by Carl G. Fisher and dubbed the "Lincoln Highway." Privately supported by the sale of certificates when begun in 1912, it was to stretch, 20 years later, 3385 miles from New York to San Francisco.

Portland cement concrete production burgeoned with increased roadbuilding. A Federal standard formula for a concrete mix was set in 1916. Concrete mixed on site had been used for road surfacing since about 1908. Central mix began to be feasible with the development of dependable motor trucks to haul the mixed concrete to the job site. The first double-drum paver, capable of handling 27 cubic feet of mix in each drum, was introduced in 1932. This doubling of paver capacity was accompanied by the development of paving trains. Huge drum mixers, fed cement and aggregate by truck, moved along on treads, pulling spreaders, levelers and finishers on rails.

In the 1920's, cement and aggregate were trucked to the site from loading bins such as this one.

Concrete mixing on the Cornell University campus, 1909.

An early paving train in Tennessee, 1929.

A similar development in productivity enabled the "black top" paving program to maintain a strong competitive position. Asphalt plants increased in size and efficiency. The 1930's saw the introduction of bituminous pavers—road machines which ingested heated bituminous-aggregate at one end and disgorged it in lane widths at the other, eliminating hand spreading on large jobs. Rollers and finishers followed to complete the paving job.

The need for mechanization to minimize labor costs had been recognized as early as 1908, when Wayne County, Michigan, paved with Portland cement concrete its first mile of highway. "More prosperous times" then had made it difficult to secure common laborers "at $2 per day of 10 hours." Better equipment reduced labor costs, but, in the early 1920's, an industry spokesman noted, it was still considered a good day when a contractor paved 350 to 400 feet, and

Concrete finishing, New Jersey.

A "portable" road plant for bituminous concrete, Florida, 1917.

1000 feet was a record.

Advocating the mechanical handling of cement, one authority stated that "on most jobs five or six men are employed in handling cement, whereas but three or four—a craneman, one or two laborers on the cars, and a hopper operator —handle the aggregate which weighs more than five times as much."

In the late 1920's, one source listed the following as the most efficient equipment for road construction jobs:

One plow, two Fresnos, blade grader, five-ton crawler tractor, scarifier, subgrader, fine finisher and roller, 5000 feet of forms, wagon and team, crane, hoppers, cement house, pump, 20,000 feet of three-inch pipe, 400 feet of two-inch hose, turntable, (cement) sack cleaner and sack baler, 20 hauling trucks, concrete finishing machine, and a repair shop. Some 46 men ("without drivers or miscellaneous") were required to operate this "most efficient equipment."

Painting centerlines in Iowa. The front-rigged model had guides traveling along the edge of the highway and the center-line, while the wheel at the rear of the vehicle applied the paint. The side-car model also guided along the side of the highway.

Along with this vast improvement in construction methods, traffic management techniques evolved. The U.S. route numbering system originated in Wisconsin in 1918 and helped travelers, map-makers and planners. It was extended throughout the United States by the American Association of State Highway Officials by the late 1920's. Center lines and lane markings were introduced; early line painters being towed by county automobiles. Traffic signals appeared to help regulate flow and reduce collisions.

An early Detroit traffic signal.

This sequence of photographs, taken at the same location, shows grubbing, clearing, excavating, backfilling and paving on Michigan Route M-25 in Huron County.

During this period, Federal-aid funds were planned and provided in two and three year stages, leading to more efficient and systematic road development. Moreover, funds were made available for planning purposes, permitting surveys that would provide the data necessary for the later forging and linking of a true interstate system.

The soil in Monona County, Iowa, was not stable enough to be controlled on a slope by erosion control techniques in existence in the early 1920's. When cuts were necessary, they were made vertical. A locally invented machine, powered by an automobile engine, operated a knife and a loading elevator. The system left something to be desired at intersections.

In the depression years of the 1930's. Federal emergency funds for the relief of unemployment, which did not require matching money from the states, helped continue road construction during a period when pressures were great within the states to divert road-user revenues to other purposes. Road needs continued. In spite of the harsh economic conditions, automobile use declined relatively little. From 1929 to 1937, registrations declined only from 26.5 million to 23.9 million vehicles.

CHAPTER 9

TOLLWAYS AND FREEWAYS

By 1940, there were 23,000,000 automobiles and trucks swarming over American roads, streets and highways. Congestion was a serious problem and, especially around large cities, it seemed to be getting worse. Street improvements seemed to give only temporary relief. The improvements made the street attractive to business, new business generated more traffic, and, in a few months, congestion was as bad as ever.

There had been large-scale improvement in the rural areas. Nevertheless, most roads closely followed the terrain, no matter what sharp curves and steep

April 1941 in Heard County, Georgia—the first paved road in the county being completed.

grades might result. Many hundreds of thousands of miles of rural roads remained unpaved.

Also by 1940, the concept of the "expressway" or "freeway" was about to come into flower.

In 1924, New York State limited traffic on the Bronx River Parkway, between New York City and White Plains, to passenger cars only. Cross traffic was eliminated, and the speed limit was set at a "liberal" 35 mph.

The idea of a high-speed motorway was further developed in toll roads and parkways built in scattered locations through the ensuing two decades.

1940 Road Show.

The Merritt Parkway, 1941.

Planning began in 1926 for the Merritt Parkway in Connecticut, intended to relieve congestion on the old Boston Post Road. A small toll was imposed, justified by the high standards followed. The highway was divided, separating opposing flows of traffic. Access was limited to designated intersections, and there was complete grade separation of all cross traffic.

At about the same time, expressway concepts began to receive serious consideration in Los Angeles. The city was growing rapidly, and the terrain permitted this growth to be predominantly horizontal. In a city of great distances, the concept grew that time—not distance—is the primary determining factor in economic transportation. By 1937, a study of the Los Angeles traffic system recommended an extensive radial freeway system, bypass routes and—a revolutionary departure—elevated roadways. Incorporating

Hollywood-Pasadena Freeway, 1949—one of the first to elevate roadway.

these ideas, and backed with state and Federal relief funds, the Arroyo Seco freeway (Pasadena Freeway) was begun in 1940.

"Freeways" raised numerous questions, some in the engineering field and some in the legal area. For example, did limited access infringe on the right of the public to enter and leave a public road? A man's property might abut the highway; yet, his closest legal access point might be several miles distant.

The point was settled, at least with respect to toll roads, with the Pennsylvania Turnpike. This state-wide, limited access divided highway was opened in 1940. Much of it was built on right-of-way abandoned by the never-completed South Pennsylvania Railroad. The turnpike did, in fact, use seven tunnels that had been bored for the railroad. Unlike the Merritt and Bronx River Parkways, the Pennsylvania Turnpike was intended from the start to serve

commercial traffic. Although a toll was imposed, truckers found it well worthwhile. It was shown that a 25-ton truck could cut fuel costs in half by using the turnpike and that it could also travel the distance in half the time. It was a good bargain for the truckers and an equally good bargain for the state—financially, the turnpike stood on its own feet. Other states began to look at the feasibility of toll roads.

Pennsylvania Turnpike, 1942.

Allegheny Tunnel.

There were other new ideas. In Chicago, the Outer Drive incorporated a variable lane separation to favor inbound traffic in the morning and outbound at night. Lane-separating curbs were raised and lowered hydraulically. This was one of many ideas that never caught on. The curbs proved expensive, difficult to maintain, and somewhat unreliable, especially under snow and ice.

The era of World War II was marked by many spectacular engineering achievements, accomplished under great pressure. Tanks, trucks and other military machines were made bigger and more powerful. The design experience was to be useful to equipment manufacturers in building the big construction machines of the post-war period.

Military construction teams performed many nearly incredible feats. One of the most spectacular was the construction of the Alcan Highway from Dawson Creek, British Columbia, to Fairbanks, Alaska, in 1942, a distance of 1526 miles. The U.S. Army Corps of Engineers completed the highway in ap-

Turnpike exit.

proximately eight months, an accomplishment which has been termed the greatest engineering feat since the construction of the Panama Canal. With temperatures ranging from 90 degrees above to 60 degrees below zero, the road was cut through mud, muskeg and permafrost. The successful completion of the Alcan Highway, according to one account, "is the story of the track-mounted bulldozer blade, for every mile was a pioneering and clearing effort, much of the way through dense forest." The post-war roadbuilding program was significantly affected by two Federal studies; one completed just before the

Chicago's Outer Drive, one curb raised, the other down.

war, the other during it.

The first, in 1939, responded to a Congressional directive that the Bureau of Public Roads study the feasibility of a national system of toll roads. As suggested by Congress, there would be three such roads from coast to coast and three more connecting the Canadian and Mexican borders. With respect to the toll road proposal, the Bureau's report was negative. The Bureau agreed, however, that there was merit in the idea of a national system of limited access roads, connecting the principal urban areas. It was thought that such a system might extend 30,000 to 40,000 miles.

This report led to a second study, this one by a commission appointed by President Franklin D. Roosevelt. In 1944, the commission recommended the construction of a "National System of Interregional Highways" extending about 40,000 miles, connecting and passing through principal cities throughout the country and "serving the national defense."

The 1944 report recommended construction to high standards to produce a system capable of handling high-speed, high-volume traffic, with an emphasis on safety.

Although the war had brought roadbuilding to a virtual standstill, Congress was looking ahead, with evident enthusiasm, to the post-war years. The Federal-Aid Highway Act of 1944 established proce-

dures for the selection of inter-city routes on the "Interregional" highway system. Also, for the first time, the 1944 Act provided Federal assistance for the extension of Federal-aid primary and secondary routes within urban areas. Up until then, the Federal-aid highway program had been strictly rural.

The seeds of the Interstate System were planted, but they were slow to germinate. Federal-aid funding was increased in the post-war years, but the backlog of highway needs was a huge one. Roads neglected during World War II had to be reconstructed. With 50-50 matching the standard for all categories of Federal aid, most states were unable to move forward with Interstate-type highways, except as toll roads. In 1954, Congress increased the Federal share payable for Interstate System projects from 50 to 60 percent.

The 1948 Road Show was the largest held up to that time. With the outlook bright for big programs, manufacturers exhibited a three-and-a-half yard power shovel, a 24-ton crawler tractor, a 30-ton vibratory roller. There were bottom-dump wagons capable of handling 20-yard loads, and a concrete paver boasting a 34-cubic foot capacity.

In the 1940's, the Portland Cement Association's development of air-entrained concrete permitted longer hauls of slower-setting concrete to meet contractors' demands for larger volumes. Multi-lane paving trains moved on rails up to 4700 feet a day.

1940's paving job on U.S. 40 in Ohio. Train consists of two Koehring pavers followed by two Jaeger concrete spreaders, two Jaeger finishers, and one Koehring Bull Float.

A modern vibratory compactor.

Asphalt pavers developed on-site, self-propelled mixing plants, multi-lane spreaders for hot mix, and vibratory rollers which not only compacted sub-soils but provided base preparation and surface finishing as well.

The telescoping boom excavator and the front-end loader were developed to largely displace the power shovel in roadbuilding.

The slip-form paver, perhaps the most dramatic innovation in Portland cement concrete paving, was conceived in 1946 by two Iowa highway engineers, James W. Johnson and Bert Myers. The paver would move along a prepared grade carrying its side forms with it. This would eliminate the need for hundreds or thousands of feet of steel forms and greatly speed the paving process. Although the paver was used in Iowa in 1949, it was not made available generally until the late 1950's.

Pavement design was greatly influenced by extensive tests carried out by highway officials, notably the WASHO (Western Association of State Highway Officials) Road Test in Idaho and the subsequent AASHO (American Association of State Highway Officials) Road Test in Illinois. Test sections of roadway were built, using various thicknesses of pavement and various materials. Under carefully controlled conditions, vehicles were driven continuously on the test tracks until the test sections were worn out. These tests were important in standardizing construction specifications among states. However, the highway officials emphasized that standardization is no panacea and recommended that states give proper consideration to the specific traffic conditions, climate, and soil characteristics of a given area. With better equipment and better design guidance, the outlook for better roads was distinctly good.

The first model of a slip-form paver, being tried on an Iowa road in 1949.

CHAPTER 10

CHEOPS SURPASSED: 42,500 NON-STOP MILES

By the early 1950's, there were 65,000,000 motor vehicles crowding American roads. Nearly 40,000 persons died annually in motor vehicle accidents, and another 1,300,000 were injured. Clearly, there was a need for more highway capacity. But the Interstate System, the best single solution to the problem of increasing highway capacity, evolved slowly. The 1954 Highway Act increased the annual authorization level for the Interstate System from $25 million to $175 million, but that was only a small fraction of what was needed. President Eisenhower appointed General Lucius Clay to head a special fact-finding advisory committee. More specifically, the Clay Committee set out to project the nation's highway needs over the next ten years and investigate the means for meeting those needs.

What was needed, the Clay Committee said, in essence, was a ten-year concentrated effort, costing an estimated $100 billion. One of the questions to be answered was whether the highway industry had the productive capacity to carry out a program of that magnitude. The American Road Builders' Association undertook an inventory of the entire industry. ARBA found that 6,200 highway contractors employed 240,000 men. They had available to them a fleet of 331,000 trucks, tractors, scrapers and other types of equipment. Equipment manufacturers had recently invested $200 million in new plants and equipment. ARBA concluded that ample surplus capacity existed.

The major shortfall, ARBA said, was in the supply of engineering manpower. It was predicted that the state highway departments would need to depend much more heavily on private engineering firms to supplement the design work turned out by highway agency personnel. With the advent of a full-scale Interstate program, this prediction was to be proven remarkably accurate.

By the middle of the 1950's, about one-fourth of the U.S. total of 3.2 million miles of road had been paved. A Bureau of Public Roads survey showed that about 450,000 miles were "low-type" bituminous surfaces, while an additional 400,000 miles were bituminous or Portland cement concrete. A small number of miles were paved with brick or stone block.

Much more needed to be done. The stumbling block was finding the money. At the 1954 Governors' Conference, President Eisenhower said the Nation should spend $50 billion to bring American roads to acceptable standards.

1950's street.

A remnant of the Dollarway Road, near
Pine Bluff, Arkansas. Listed in the
National Register of Historic Places,
the Dollarway Road is an early example of
Portland cement concrete paving. The
remaining sections resemble a sidewalk
through wooded terrain.

The governors and the Congress recognized the need for roads, but the price tag seemed awesome.

The landmark legislation was the Federal-Aid Highway Act of 1956. In one comprehensive package, it established a time-table for the completion of the Interstate System, substantially increased Federal-aid funding for both Interstate and other Federal-aid roads, and provided a mechanism for raising the money.

The fund-raising mechanism was the Highway Trust Fund, similar in concept to the dedicated highway funds which had been set up earlier in most of the states. Special Federal taxes on highway users would be placed in the trust fund. It was intended that these taxes would be increased, lowered or modified to bring in exactly enough revenue to support the highway construction program and to spread the burden equitably among various classes of users. (These good intentions were not entirely carried out. Beginning in 1967, the Executive Branch impounded billions of Highway Trust Fund dollars as a means of holding down Federal deficits.)

The 1956 Act proposed a "balanced" program between Interstate and non-Interstate construction without defining

exactly what was meant by "balanced." Federal authorizations were heavy on the Interstate side of the scale, but they needed to be, for the Federal share of the Interstate costs was set at 90 percent, while non-Interstate construction continued at 50-50 matching.

As developed in the House of Representatives, the plan called for the completion of the Interstate System in 16 years, with authorizations spread over 13 years. Thus, the last authorization contemplated was for the fiscal year ending June 30, 1969. These funds would be fully expended and the roads open to traffic by June 30, 1972. It was expected that Trust Fund revenues would climb steadily with the increase in traffic. Construction costs, on the other hand, would peak early, then level off. The Highway Trust Fund, therefore, would be in a deficit position during the early years of the program.

This deficit spending proposal disturbed Sen. Harry F. Byrd of Virginia, a staunch fiscal conservative and chairman of the Senate Finance Committee. The "Byrd Amendment" limited construction progress to the capacity of the Highway Trust Fund. The program was to operate strictly on a cash-on-the-barrelhead basis.

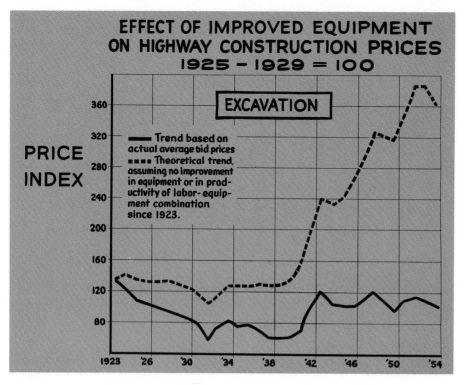

EFFECT OF IMPROVED EQUIPMENT ON HIGHWAY CONSTRUCTION PRICES
1925 – 1929 = 100

PRICE INDEX

EXCAVATION

—— Trend based on actual average bid prices
▪▪▪▪ Theoretical trend, assuming no improvement in equipment or in productivity of labor- equipment combination since 1923.

360
320
280
240
200
160
120
80

1923 '26 '30 '34 '38 '42 '46 '50 '54

In 1956, the cost of completing the Interstate System was estimated to be about $27 billion. The estimated cost has more than tripled. This is partly due to general price inflation (the highway cost index doubled between 1967 and 1974), but also is due to higher standards and social and environmental concerns.

The Interstate System was seen as the first step in a grand plan to modernize the entire highway system of the nation. Although the Interstate System will comprise only about 1.2 percent of the road mileage in the United States, it will carry almost one-fourth of the total highway traffic. Thus, it is intended as the foundation of the total modernized highway network.

One enthusiastic engineer called the Interstate program the most extensive engineering project since the Great Pyramid was built by Cheops in 2600 B.C.

The accelerated highway program encouraged the development and use of a new generation of road construction machinery. It tended to be bigger, more powerful and, at the same time, capable of greater precision. The torque converter permitted the smooth application of

The vibratory roller, shown working at night, is a modern descendent of the old steam roller. Vibrations, variable depending on soil characteristics, can double the compactive force without increasing weight.

BUFFALO BOMAG

power for large and varying loads.
The track-type tractor, pioneer of the industry, continued to move upward in size and power. Machines that started out as 230 flywheel horsepower crawlers in the mid 1950's became the more than 400 flywheel horsepower crawlers of the mid 1970's. Smaller crawlers stretched downward into comparatively light horsepower in order to meet the requirements of lighter earthmoving projects.

Tractor-drawn scrapers were still a vigorous part of the earthmoving scene in the 1950's, but self-propelled scrapers were predominant by the 1970's.

Another basic change took place in the ripper which, for many years, was towed, usually by a crawler tractor. In more recent times, the ripper has more often been attached to and integrated with the crawler.

Similarly, the towed sheep's foot roller has largely given way to the self-propelled compactor. Many kinds of compactors have been developed—the grid roller, vibratory, the smooth steel drums, the multi-tired pneumatic, the heavy pneumatic, the towed tamping foot and the high speed tamping foot.

This Euclid bottom dump can haul a heaped load of 54 cubic yards at speeds up to 40 mph.

A 35-ton rear-dump truck at a rock crusher.

The first front-end loaders were primitive by today's standards. The 1950's saw the first moves toward an integrated crawler tractor and bucket. Progress was swift through the 1960's, with many manufacturers moving into the market. Bucket capacity increased from a rather awkward one cubic yard to a smooth and rapidly delivered five cubic yards. The wheel loader experienced similar evolvement and, because of its maneuverability and great appetite for materials rapidly expanded to a ten cubic yard machine. Special buckets and conditions permit some wheel loaders to handle loads of up to 24 cubic yards. Over the past two decades, wheel loaders have worked their way into many job situations that probably were not antici-

pated when these machines were first introduced.

The familiar motor grader continued to improve and take on new functions. As it became larger and more powerful, it also displayed more maneuverability through articulation and power shift. Motor graders now work to very close tolerances, engaging in finish grading that challenges the operator's capabilities.

The largest of all the load carriers in construction earthmoving are the wheel tractor scrapers. Introduced just before World War II, this machine has played an important part in holding down the average cost of moving a yard of earth. Early models moved five to seven cubic yards; by the early 1970's, the capacity figure had reached 54 cubic yards.

This CMI motor grader was built to fine-grade to very close tolerances while being adaptable to perform heavy-duty bladework as well.

Grade trimmer. This adaptation of the motor grader does a fast, accurate trimming job.

Although the standard scraper with a single engine is still popular, it has been challenged in recent years by the tandem-powered and push-pull scrapers. Meanwhile, elevating scrapers have been developed which load up to 32 cubic yards and move these loads at speeds up to 34 mph.

If the total yards of earth moved in the United States during the past 20 years could be calculated, the wheel tractor scraper would undoubtedly show up as the workhorse earthmover.

Since the late 1960's, the excavator has moved rapidly to an important position on the rapidly changing earthmoving scene. The United States lagged behind other countries in the development and use of the hydraulic excavator, but improvement in mobility and efficiency has been rapid. With capabilities ranging upward to 10 cubic yards, excavators have filled a real need in trenching and ditching operations.

Early motor trucks used in highway construction were generally limited to the load limits in effect for highway travel. These limits, of course, do not affect the capacity of load-hauling trucks and tractors designed for off-highway use. Machines loading more than 100 tons are now in use by highway contractors. Even these behemoths are dwarfed by haulers of up to 250 ton capacities used in the mining industry.

As earthmoving capacity escalated, the basic power plant has remained the diesel engine. From its introduction to the construction equipment market, by Caterpillar in the early 1930's, the diesel engine has gradually improved in power and efficiency. Of the many modifications, the one probably most worthy of mention is the introduction of turbocharged diesel engines in the mid 1950's. Available horsepower increased by almost one-half.

A Bucyrus-Erie hydraulic hoe on water-sewer line construction near Leadville, Colorado.

This Buffalo soil stabilizer performs two operations with one pass. The existing surface material is scarified, then mixed with a binder. After compaction, the sub-base is ready.

During the past 20 years, most of the changes in earthmovers have had little effect on basic configuration—the machines look a lot the same. One exception was the addition of rollover protective structures, required by Federal regulation. Outstanding improvements include sealed and lubricated track, the torsion bar bulldozer, motor grader automatic blade control, the sleeve metering fuel system, the variable capacity torque converter and the beadless tire.

In the highly competitive field of earth-moving equipment, hundreds of millions of dollars are spent each year in research and engineering. Each manufacturer offers exclusive special features. One company (Caterpillar) reported that it holds more than 1,100 U.S. patents covering features on its basic products.

Comparable improvements have been made in paving equipment.

The slip-form paver was by no means the only major contributor to more efficient Portland cement concrete paving operations. In addition, conventional paving trains were greatly improved.

A form-riding paving train of the late 1950's. The paver (left), fed by a convoy of batching trucks, mixed the concrete. The other machines, in order, are the spreader, finishers, a drag machine to add texture and, lastly, a curing machine to coat the surface.

With greater automation and more flexible power plants, central mixing with both tilting drum and turbine mixers became more economical and quality control of the product became more effective. Research stimulated by the U.S. Bureau of Public Roads confirmed that mixing times could be reduced appreciably without affecting quality.

The pre-blending of aggregates and cement on the belt conveyor reduces required mixing time.

Control panels in the trailer operate the entire Rex central mix plant. Cement is shot under pressure from the bulker tank (left) to the cement bins at center.

The Portland cement concrete paving site in the 1970's is highly mechanized, with specialized equipment geared to the job. The paving train may include mesh and dowel installers, long-wheel-base float-type finishers, internal vibrators, mechanical membrane sprayers and a variety of concrete sawing equipment.

Curbs and sidewalks can be slip-formed too. The Curbmaster Robot was introduced in 1969.

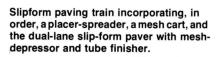

Slipform paving train incorporating, in order, a placer-spreader, a mesh cart, and the dual-lane slip-form paver with mesh-depressor and tube finisher.

In 1950, the record paving day was 4700 feet of pavement 11 feet wide. By 1974, the American Concrete Paving Association's "Mile A Day Club" included 70 contractors. The record day's work was 4.7 miles of pavement 24 feet wide, placed on Interstate Route 80 in Idaho. (It was a long day; the contractor worked 23 hours.)

S.J. Groves at work, 1971, on the Southern Tier Expressway near Bath, New York.

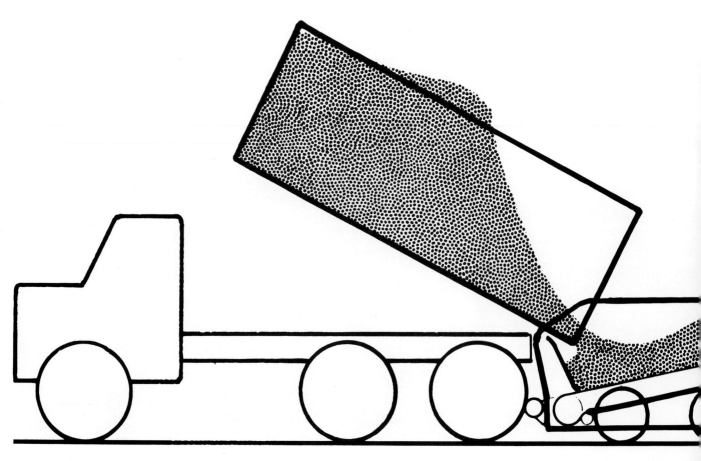

The versatility of the slip-form paver has improved in recent years. It is now used in producing continuous reinforced concrete paving, as well as to meet other specifications. Variations of slip-forming are used for the production of medians and curb-and-gutter.

Parallel advances have come about in bituminous concrete paving.

One particularly notable development is the automatic screed, or leveling device, developed by a Kansas state highway engineer, Frank M. Drake, in the late 1950's. Following a string-line laid along the grade, a device on the side of the asphalt paver electronically senses variations in grade and surface and, by operating servo motors at either end of the screed to adjust its height and angle, levels the concrete to exacting specifications. Automatic screeds permit leveling to within a tenth of an inch over 50 feet. The development of the dryer drum, or turbulent mass, process promises new economies in the asphalt mixing process, through the elimination of hot screening and hot bins. In the dryer

Iowa Manufacturing Company built this first asphalt paver with vibratory screed.

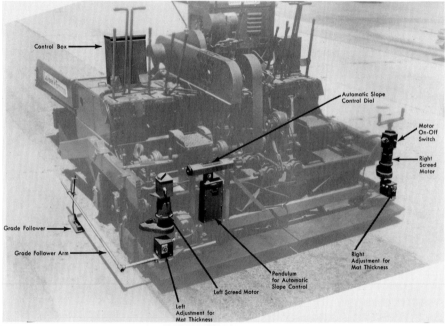

Control Box

Automatic Slope
Control Dial

Motor
On-Off
Switch

Right
Screed
Motor

Grade Follower

Grade Follower Arm

Left
Adjustment for
Mat Thickness

Left Screed Motor

Pendulum
for Automatic
Slope Control

Right
Adjustment for
Mat Thickness

Details of one type of automatic paver control system. The grade follower (left) senses irregularities and signals the control box, which makes the necessary corrections.

Automatic grade and slope control.

drum process, aggregates and bituminous materials are both heated and mixed in a single drum, rather than separately.

Asphalt batching cycles have been fully automated. After setting controls and loading, the operator need only push a button, all necessary information having been stored electronically.

Improvements in asphalt mixing processes were needed to fit the needs of improved paving machines. Modern equipment, with spreaders and vibratory compactor working in tandem, can lay pavement 30-feet wide in one pass, or, to say it another way, 500 tons of asphalt in an hour—"just as fast as we can haul it in," one contractor noted.

A Barber-Greene drum mixing plant.

Power Curber with tailgate loader. This asphalt curb was placed for water control on Interstate Route 5, south of Medford, Oregon.

Self-erecting automated asphalt plants were developed which can be transported to the job site and set up in a day to pour out hot mix the next.
Much tedious labor has been eliminated through the use of more efficient

The self-erecting asphalt plant: (1) columns and screen-bin section in place;

(2) columns being raised;

(3) columns up and fastened together;

(4) screen and bin section raised;

machinery and techniques, at the same time resulting in better roads at lower cost. (But old ways die hard. It was reported in 1974 that a contractor completed clean-up work on an Interstate project using a 1925 Fresno.)

(5) mixer/batcher section spotted for raising;

(6) tower completed, hot elevator ready for raising;

(7) mineral filler elevator being raised;

(8) ready to work!

There are more than 60,000 bridges on the Interstate System, including the many overpass structures. With so many bridges to be built, refinements in bridge design were almost inevitable. Even more significant, the Interstate design concept calls for the elimination of sharp curves; therefore, the bridge must be built to fit the alignment of the highway, rather than bending the road to fit

Philadelphia's Schuylkill Expressway, under construction.

the most economical bridge site. Design standards for the Interstate System were set high at the beginning of the program, strongly influenced by turnpike designs. With more experience in handling traffic on highways with full access control, standards were set even higher to incorporate new safety features. The 1956 Highway Act required that Interstate highways be designed to carry the traffic loads anticipated in 1975. As 1975 became nearer, the law was amended to require designing for traffic 20 years ahead. Even so, it has been necessary to widen some Interstate segments. Several things got in the way; and, like the National Road 150 years earlier, the Interstate System's construction did not proceed on schedule, within cost estimates, or without oppositon.

On one point all could agree: Travel on the Interstate System was different. The high design standards encompassed higher safe operating speeds, and travel time was further reduced by the elimination of intersections at grade and the separation of opposing traffic lanes. Some complained that travel was too much separated from the country-side. One no longer passed through the main streets of towns along the way or the head of the farmer's lane. Federal law sought to beautify the highway by banning billboards, but even that action, according to some, took some of the local flavor out of traveling.

The principal opposition to the Interstate System arose with respect to certain specific urban links, and was partly based on the premise that the Interstate System did its job too well. By making it easier for automobile passengers to reach the center city, the Interstate encouraged them to live out in the suburbs, it was reasoned. The central city was burdened with the problem of providing parking and saddled with other undesirable side effects. Proponents insisted that the benefits far out-weighed the disadvantages.

Many political leaders voiced concern about a lack of coordination in transportation development. Were highways being planned and designed to fit into an integrated total transportation plan?

Interstate Route 95 between Augusta and Waterville, Maine.

Beginning in 1962, Federal law required that Federal-aid highways in the larger urban areas be constructed to conform to comprehensive, continuing planning processes which would take into account the needs of all modes of transportation. In 1966, Congress authorized the establish of a Federal Department of Transportation, looking toward the closer coordination of transportation development. About half of the States had followed the Federal example by 1975, bringing their highway departments into new multi-modal transportation agencies.

Ever since the automobile began to take to the roads in large number, the highway agencies have struggled to build and improve roads to keep pace with the demand. Consequently, cost-effectiveness has been a matter of paramount concern. In recent years, spurred by a new national interest in preserving the natural environment, many highway dollars have been spent in esthetic and environmental features. At the national level, it all comes together in the environmental impact statement, the preparation of which requires public participation in and inter-agency reviews of highway location and design decisions.

A burning issue still: Should travelers view the scenery (Arizona here) or the billboards.

Bridge and tunnel in Arizona.

Interstate Route 430 bridge across the Arkansas River at Little Rock.

West Portal of the Eisenhower Tunnel on Interstate Route 70, 60 miles west of Denver.

The Chesapeake Bay Bridge under construction. The span made ocean beaches much more accessible to Washington and Baltimore residents.

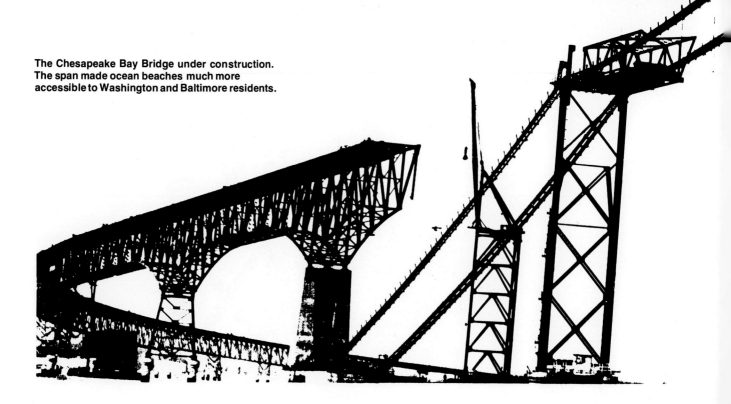

Despite new complications, engineering and construction marvels still are achieved. Interstate Route 60 crosses the Continental Divide in Colorado through the Eisenhower Tunnel. The Chesapeake Bay Bridge-Tunnel, completed in 1964, carries motor vehicle traffic beneath two channels, with bridges covering the remainder of the distance between Norfolk and Cape Charles, on Virginia's Eastern Shore. Bridges like the award-winning span between Kittery, Maine, and Portsmouth, New Hampshire, successfully combine utility and beauty.

Since the invention of the automobile, traffic accidents have taken more than 2,000,000 lives. Inadequate roads are part of the problem. An important part of the highway construction program is aimed directly at the matter of eliminating hazards, such as rail-highway grade crossings, narrow bridges and roadside obstacles.

The 38-foot-long bottom chord, 3 feet deep, 2½ feet wide and weighing 13 tons, begins the final stage of the steelwork on the Piscataqua River Bridge between Portsmouth, N.H., and Kittery, Me. Raised with it is the traditional final-steelwork symbol—the American flag.

Despite remarkable achievements and tremendous progress, the development of U.S. transportation facilities is not keeping pace with national needs. Former Secretary of Transportation John A. Volpe was fond of saying that we needed to double U.S. transportation capacity to meet the needs of 1990, or, that we would have to provide as much capacity between 1970 and 1990 as had been developed in all the years previous.

A nearly completed bridge on Interstate Route 81, near Harrisburg, Pa.

An easy gradient through rough country in Arizona.

Landscaping makes this interchange green in Arizona desert country.

A nighttime scene at the Eisenhower Interchange, near Harrisburg, Pa.

All of these pictures were taken at the same location on Route 1 in New Jersey.

(1). Early 1920's.

(2). 1933.

(3) 1938.

(4) 1972.

Pittsburgh Point. One of the Nation's highest concentration of bridges.

No instant transportation construction boom resulted from this exhortation. In 1975, a high official of the Federal Highway Administration commented that the highway construction program was not extensive enough to even maintain the present level of service. It is all too evident that the effort to complete the Interstate System has left many other road needs unmet.

This, then, is an unfinished history.
Much has been done, but much remains
to be done.

The San Juan-Ponce Toll Highway in
Puerto Rico passes through rugged
mountain ranges.

SOURCES OF INFORMATION

The sources from which material was derived for this pictorial history are widespread and varied. Many of the richer accounts were cited in the introduction. Books were the principal resource for covering the period to the early 1900's. Numerous professional and governmental documents, along with such histories as Morison's and Rae's, provided the basic material for the early 20th Century, until World War II. From that period until the present, journal articles, news accounts and the reminiscences of many individuals, both in government and in private business, served as the original sources of information.

The principal printed sources of information are cited below.

AASHO-AGC-ARBA Joint Subcommittee on Construction Costs, "Cost-Cutting Suggestions on Highway Construction," August, 1973.

Adams, Lee, "History," (private communications from WABCO), Peoria, Ill., 1972.

American Road Builders' Association, "Proceedings of the Eighth Annual Convention of the American Road Builders' Association," The American Road Builders' Association, New York, N.Y., February 2, 1912.

Angle, Paul M., *The American Reader: From Columbus to Today,* Rand McNally & Co., New York, N.Y., 1958.

Asphalt Institute, The, "Asphalt Paving Manual (MS-8)", The Asphalt Institute, College Park, Md., August, 1965.

Dunbar, Seymour, *A History of Travel in America,* Greenwood Press, New York, N.Y., 1968.

Finch, James Kip, *The Story of Engineering,* Doubleday & Company, Inc., Garden City, N.Y., 1960.

Gillis, L.R., and Spicklemire, L.S., "Slip-Form Paving in the United States," Technical Bulletin No. 263, American Road Builders' Association, Washington, D.C., 1967.

Hadden, Samuel C., "The History and Accomplishment of Twenty-Five Years of Federal Aid for Highways," American Association of State Highway Officials, Washington, D.C., November, 1944.

Hindley, Geoffrey, *A History of Roads,* The Citadel Press, Secaucus, N.J., 1971.

Holbrook, Stewart H., *The Story of American Railroads,* Bonanza Books, New York, N.Y., 1968.

Holland, Rupert Sargent, *Historic Railroads,* Macrae Smith Company, Philadelphia, Pa., 1927.

Hulbert, Archer Butler, *Historic Highways of America,* originally published in 1904, AMS Press, New York, N.Y., 1971.

Indiana Highway Constructors, Inc., *1924-1974, Serving Indiana through 50 Years of Highway Progress,* Indiana Highway Constructors, Inc., Indianapolis, Ind., 1974.

Jenkins, James T., Jr., "The Story of Roads," American Road Builders' Association, Washington, D.C., 1967.

Jordan, Philip D., *The National Road,* Bobbs-Merrill Company, New York, N.Y., 1948.

MacDonald, Thomas H., "The History and Development of Road Building in the United States," Paper No. 1685, American Society of Civil Engineers, October 6, 1926.

Morison, Samuel Eliot, *The Oxford History of the American People,* Oxford University Press, New York, N.Y., 1965.

National Interregional Highway Committee, *Interregional Highways,* House Document No. 379, 78th Congress, U.S. Government Printing Office, Washington, D.C., 1944.

Oglesby, Clarkson H., and Hewes, Laurence I., *Highway Engineering,* 2nd ed., John Haley & Sons, Inc., New York, N.Y., 1963.

Rae, John N., *The Road and the Car in American Life,* M.I.T. Press, Cambridge, Mass., 1971.

Sessions, Gordon M., and the Institute of Traffic Engineers, "Traffic Devices: Historical Aspects Thereof," Institute of Traffic Engineers, Washington, D.C., 1971.

Shank, William H., P.E., "Historic Bridges of Pennsylvania," Buchart-Horn, York, Pa., 1966.

Shank, William H., P.E., "Indian Trails to Super Highways," Buchart-Horn, York, Pa., 1967.

Smartt, Vaughn, "Great Moments in Construction History," Constructor, Vol. LV, No. 8, August, 1973, Associated General Contractors of America, Washington, D.C.

U.S. Bureau of the Census, *Historical Statistics of the United States,* U.S. Government Printing Office, Washington, D.C., 1960.

U.S. Department of Agriculture, "Toll Roads and Free Roads," House Document No. 272, 76th Congress, U.S. Government Printing Office, Washington, D.C., 1939.

West Virginia Department of Highways, "A Highway History of West Virginia from Colonial Time to the Present," West Virginia Department of Highways, Charleston, W.Va., December, 1973.

Woods, Kenneth B., Ed., *Highway Engineering Handbook,* McGraw-Hill, New York, N.Y., 1960.

ILLUSTRATION CREDITS

The cover design is from a mural by Paul Takacs in the lobby of the ARBA Building, 525 School Street, S.W., Washington, D.C. The front end paper is a reproduction of a photograph in the Library of Congress showing construction of a Portland cement concrete road in Durham County, N.C., in 1919. The back end paper, from a South Carolina Highway Department photograph, depicts the construction of an access road to the Savannah River Plant, Aiken County, S.C., about 1950. The embellishments to the Table of Contents are miniaturizations of large line drawings by Walt Pittman, El Monte, Cal. Several abbreviations are used in the listing which follows:

ARBA. American Road Builders' Association.

LOC. Library of Congress. In the case of both the Library of Congress and National Archives listings, some of the photographs were taken by photographers who, then or subsequently, were widely recognized for their work. Where the names are available, they are listed.

USBPR. U.S. Bureau of Public Roads Collection, National Archives.

USDOT. U.S. Department of Transportation. Reproductions of oil paintings from this source are part of a series of 109 paintings completed by Carl Rakeman over a 26-year period, beginning in 1939, when he was employed by the Bureau of Public Roads.

Introduction
Page 4, American Automobile Association.

Chapter 1
Page 6, William H. Shank; 7, LOC—Arthur Rothstein, USBPR; 8-9, USDOT; 10, Paul B. Reinhold Collection; 10-11, William H. Shank; 11, USBPR; 12, USDOT, William H. Shank; 13, ARBA; 14, USDOT.

Chapter 2
Page 16, Paul B. Reinhold Collection; 17, ARBA; 18, USDOT; 19, USBPR; 20-21, USDOT; 22-23, USBPR—Carl Mydans; 23, USDOT.

Chapter 3
Page 24, USDOT; 25, LOC, USDOT; 26, ARBA; 26-27, National Archives; 27, ARBA; 28-29, USDOT; 30-31, LOC; 32, USBPR—J.K. Hilliers, Jr.; 33, William H. Shank.

Chapter 4
Pages 34-35, USBPR; 36, USBPR, Paul B. Reinhold Collection; 36-37, USBPR; 37, ARBA; 38, California Department of Transportation; 38-39, USBPR; 40, USBPR; (2) ARBA; 40-41, USBPR; 41, ARBA, USBPR (2); 42, USBPR (illustrations appeared originally in issues of *Scientific American);* 42-43, USBPR; 43, USBPR, Iowa Department of Transportation.

Chapter 5
Page 44, USBPR; 45, Ohio Department of Transportation, Library of Congress; 46, USBPR; 46-47, William H. Shank; 47, USBPR (from *Harper's,* 1895); 48-49, 50, USBPR; 51, Idaho Department of Transportation; 52-53, USBPR; 54, USBPR, Library of Congress; 54-55, Oregon State Highway Division; 55, USBPR; 56, WABCO; 56-57, USBPR, L.E. Boglein; 57, USBPR; 58-59, Ohio Department of Transportation; 60-63, USBPR.

Chapter 6
Pages 64-65, California Department of Transportation; 65, Florida Transportation Builders Association; 66, Florida Department of Transportation, USBPR; 66-67, USBPR; 67, Portland Cement Association; 68-69, California Department of Transportation; 70-71, California Department of Transportation; 72, USBPR; 72-73, USBPR—C.C. Akles; 73, USBPR; 74, USBPR—J.K. Hillers; 75, Oklahoma Department of Transportation, Florida Department of Transportation.

Chapter 7
Page 76, William H. Shank; 77, ARBA, Library of Congress; 78, USBPR; 78-79, LOC; 79-80, ARBA; 81, Courtesy of *Constructor* Magazine, The Associated General Contractors of America; 82-85, Library of Congress.

Chapter 8
Page 86, USBPR (from *Scientific American);* 86-87, Ohio Department of Transportation; 88, ARBA; 88-92, Caterpillar Tractor Co.; 93, Maine Department of Transportation; 94-96, WABCO; 97, Nebraska Department of Roads, Oregon Division of Highways; 98-99, WABCO; 100-101, Ohio Department of Transportation; 102-103, Florida Transportation Builders Association; 104, LOC; 104-105, Caterpillar Tractor Co.; 105, ARBA; 106-107, Idaho Department of Transportation; 107, John P. Moss; 108-109, Scott Bridge Co.; 110-111, LOC; 111, Iowa Department of Transportation; 112, Portland Cement Association; 113, USBPR; 114-115, Texas Highway Department, New Jersey Department of Transportation; Florida Department of Transportation; 116-117, Iowa Department of Transportation; 118, USDOT; 118-119, Iowa Department of Transportation; 119, Institute of Traffic Engineers; 120, Oregon Division of Highways, Huron County (Mich.) Road Commission; 120-121, LOC—Marion Post Wolcott; 122-123, Iowa Department of Transportation.

Chapter 9
Page 124-125, USBPR; 125, Florida Transportation Builders Association; 126-127, LOC; 128-129, USDOT; 130-131, LOC; 132, Paul Reinhold Collection, LOC; 133, LOC; 134-137, PCA; 138-139, USBPR; 139, Ingersoll-Rand Co.; 140-141, USBPR: 142, Portland Cement Association; 143, Iowa Manufacturing Co.

Chapter 10
Page 144, Ingersoll-Rand Co.; 145, USBPR, Arkansas Highway Department; 146-147, Hercules Powder Co.; 148, Koehring Co.; 149, Euclid, Inc.; 150, Caterpillar Tractor Co.; 151, CMI Corp., Caterpillar Tractor Co.; 152-153, CMI Corp.; 154, Euclid, Inc., Bucyrus-Erie Co.; 155, Caterpillar Tractor Co., Mack Truck Co.; 156-157, Koehring Co.; 158-159, Caterpillar Tractor Co.; 160-161, Rexnord, Inc.; 161, Rexnord, Inc.; 162-163, CMI Corp.; 164, Curbmaster of America, Inc., CMI Corp.; 164-165, CMI Corp.; 165, S.J. Groves & Sons Co., Rexnord, Inc.; 166-167, Midland Machinery Co.; 168, Iowa Manufacturing Co. (2), The Asphalt Institute; 168-169, Iowa Manufacturing Co.; 169, The Asphalt Institute; 169, Power Curbers, Inc., Rexnord, Inc.; 170-171, Iowa Manufacturing Co., 172, S.J. Groves & Sons Co.; 172-175, Commonwealth of Pennsylvania; 176, Arkansas Department of Highways; 177, Louisiana Highway Department; 178-179, Maine Department of Transportation; 180-181, Arizona Department of Transportation; 182, Arkansas Highway Department, Colorado Highway Department; 182-183, USBPR; 184, Maine Department of Transportation; 185, Bethlehem Steel Corp.; 186-187, Maine Department of Transportation; 188, Arizona Department of Transportation; 189, Commonwealth of Pennsylvania, Arizona Department of Transportation; 190-191, Commonwealth of Pennsylvania; 192-193, New Jersey Department of Transportation; 194-195, Commonwealth of Pennsylvania; 196, Edwards and Kelcey; 196-197, Tippetts-Abbett-McCarthy-Stratton.

Patrons
Pages 200-202, Nebraska Department of Roads; 203, American Automobile Association, Nebraska Department of Roads; 204, Institute of Traffic Engineers, Nebraska Department of Roads; 205, Institute of Traffic Engineers; 206, Nebraska Department of Roads.

PATRONS

S.M. Abell,
Coles County Superintendent
of Highways.
Charleston, Ill.
Adams Construction Company,
Roanoke, Va.
E.J. Adcock, Adcock &
Campbell, Inc., Jackson, Miss.
**J.S. Alberici
Construction Co., Inc.,**
St. Louis, Mo.
Alabama Road Builders' Assn.,
Montgomery, Ala.
Albert Brothers Contractors, Inc.,
Salem, Va.
The Allen Co., Winchester, Ky.
J.W. Allen, Jr.,
J.W. Allen Construction Co.,
Lakeland, Fla.
Allied Chemical Corp.,
Industrial Chemicals Div.,
Paving Mats Dept., Morristown, N.J.
Buck Allison, Inc.,
Kingston Springs, Tenn.
Aman Bros., Inc., Covina, Calif.
Ames & Webb, Inc., Norfolk, Va.
American Concrete Pipe Association,
Arlington, Va.
American Consulting Engineers, Inc.,
Indianapolis, Ind.

Appalachian Construction Co., Inc.,
Wise, Va.
**Archrock Paving &
Construction Co., Inc.,**
Lewiston, Pa.
Arcon Construction Co., Inc.,
Mora, Minn.
**Arizona Transportation &
Traffic Institute,**
University of Arizona, Tucson, Ariz.
Armco Steel Corp., Middletown, Ohio
L.G. Arnold, Eau Claire, Wis.
Reginald Arnold, San Francisco, Ca.
Ashmore Brothers, Inc.,
Greenville, S.C.
The Asphalt Institute,
College Park, Md.
**Associated General Contractors of
America, Carolinas Branch, Inc.,**
Charlotte, N.C.
**Associated General Contractors of
America, Texas Highway-Heavy
Branch,** Austin, Texas
Associated Pennsylvania Constructors,
Harrisburg, Pa.
Associated Sand and Gravel Co.,
Everett, Wash.
Atlas Powder Company, Dallas, Texas
Atlas-Reinhold, Inc.,
Pittsburgh, Pa.

Baker-Wibberley & Assoc., Inc.,
Hagerstown, Md.
Ballenger Corp., Greenville, S.C.
**The Baltimore Asphalt
Paving Company,** Baltimore, Md.
Charles L. Barber & Associates, Inc.,
Toledo, Ohio
Barber-Greene Company, Aurora, Ill.
**Barge, Waggoner, Sumner & Cannon,
Engineers and Planners,**
Nashville, Tenn.
Barnhill Contracting Co., Inc.,
Tarboro, N.C.
J.C. Bates & Son, Contractors,
Cullman, Ala.
Bay-Con Industries, Inc.,
Tampa, Fla.
C.E. Beckman, Machinery Corp.,
Dominion Rd.
Brighton, Mich.
Ben-Tom Corporation,
Columbus, Ohio
Benward of Nashville, Inc.,
Nashville, Tenn.
Harlo P. Beshenbossel,
P.E., Ret., F.H.W.A.,
Morrisville, Pa.
Bester-Long, Inc., Hagerstown, Md.
Bethlehem Steel Corp.,
Bethlehem, Pa.
Bituminous Surface Treating Co.,
Inver Grove Hghts., Minn.
W.E. Blain & Sons, Inc.,
Mount Olive, Miss.
Blakemore Construction Corp.,
Richmond, Va.
D.H. Blattner & Sons, Inc.,
Avon, Minn.

Blauvelt Engineering Co.,
New York, N.Y.
Blythe Brothers Co.,
Charlotte, N.C.
**Board of County Road Commissioners
of the County of Wayne, Mich.**
Jos. D. Bonness, Inc.,
Wauwatosa, Wis.
Bowyer-Johnson-Kimes, Inc.,
Jackson, Tenn.
W.G. Bowers, Foster & Creighton Co.,
Nashville, Tenn.
J.F. Brady, Amerace Corp.,
Signal Products Div., Niles, Ill.
Brewer and Brewer Sons, Inc.,
Chillicothe, Ohio
Bridge Builders, Inc.,
McMinnville, Tenn.
The Bridge Construction Corp.,
Augusta, Me.
William E. Brinkmann,
Brinkmann Engineering,
Oconomowoc, Wis.
Buchart-Horn, York, Pa.
Ray W. Burgess, Baton Rouge, La.
A.B. Burton Co., Inc.,
Lynchburg, Va.
Herbert W. Busching, Head,
Department of Civil Engineering,
Clemson University, Clemson, S.C.
Burlington Asphalt Corporation,
Mount Holly, N.J.
William C.M. Butler, Jr.,
Central Penn Industries,
Hazelton, Pa.
Donald V. Buttenheim,
Buttenheim Publishing Corp.,
Pittsfield, Mass.
Joe T. Byrne, Jr.,
Sandar Inc.,
Omaha, Neb.

Caddell & Jackson Company,
Jacksonville, Fla.
Cadillac Asphalt Paving Co.,
Novi, Mich.
E.B. Cape, Houston, Texas
Capeletti Bros., Inc., Hialeah, Fla.
Capitol Engineering Corp.,
Dillsburg, Pa.
Capitol Grading Co., Inc.,
Butler, Wis.
Carolina Bridge Co.,
Orangeburg, S.C.
Caterpillar Tractor Co.,
Peoria, Ill.
CE Maguire, Inc., Waltham, Mass.
Central Penn Industries,
Hazleton, Pa.
C.F.W. Construction Co., Inc.,
Fayetteville, Tenn.
Chapman Contracting Co.,
Tampa, Fla.
E.M. Chastain,
Homer L. Chastain & Assoc.,
Decatur, Ill.
Cherry Hill Sand & Gravel Co., Inc.,
Jessup, Md.
Lewis M. Chittim, Helena, Mont.
Cianbro Corporation, Pittsfield, Me.
**Civil Engineering and
Engineering Mechanics Department,
Montana State University,**
Bozeman, Mont.
Clark Equipment Company,
Benton Harbor, Mich.
James G. Clark, Clark, Dietz & Assoc.,
Urbana, Ill.
Clough Associates, Albany, New York
CMI Corporation,
Oklahoma City, Okla.

Codell Construction Co.,
Winchester, Ky.
Columbia Paving, Inc.,
Lake City, Fla.
J.L. Cone, Jr., Tampa, Fla.
J.W. Conner & Sons, Inc.,
Tampa, Fla.
Construction Equipment Magazine,
Chicago, Ill.
**The Contractors Assn. of
Eastern Pennsylvania,**
Philadelphia, Pa.
**The Contractors Association of
West Virginia,**
Charleston, West Va.
B.G. Coon Construction Co.,
Luzerne, Pa.
Cooper & Woodruff, Inc.,
Amarillo, Texas
Cornell-Young Company, Inc.,
Macon, Ga.
Corson & Gruman Company,
Washington, D.C.
Corum and Edwards, Inc.,
Madisonville, Ky.
**County Engineers Association
of Ohio,** Columbus, Ohio
Craggs & Phelan Construction Co.,
Ocala, Fla.
Arthur E. Crawford,
Central Paving Company,
West Branch, Mich.
W.T. Cutchin, Sr.,
W.T. Cutchin & Assoc., Inc.,
Dyersburg, Tenn.
Curtin & Johnson, Inc.,
Washington, D.C.
Charles Dwight Curtiss,
Medford Leas, N.J.

Daily & Associates, Engineers, Inc.,
Champaign-Peoria, Ill.
Dr. Olin K. Dart, Jr.,
Louisiana State University,
Baton Rouge, La.
Russell F. Davis, Inc., Contractor,
Lafayette, Ind.
R.R. Dawson Bridge Co.,
Bloomfield, Ky.
Decker Construction Co.,
Columbus, Ohio
N.A. Degerstrom, Inc.,
Spokane, Wa.
Deleuw, Cather & Co.,
Chicago, Ill.
Dewey Jordan, Inc., Frederick, Md.
Lloyd and Sandra Dixon, Engineers,
Springfield, Ill.
T.E. Donnelly,
Greiner Engineering Sciences, Inc.,
Baltimore, Md. and Tampa, Fla.
B.M. Dornblatt, Consulting Engineers,
New Orleans, La.
Denton Construction Co.,
Grosse Point, Mich.
Dow Chemical Co., Midland, Mich.
Ronald E. Draper, Sandor, Inc.,
Amarillo, Texas

East Hudson Parkway Authority,
Pleasantville, N.Y.
Edwards and Kelcey, Newark, N.J.
John E. Eisenhour, Jr.
Eisenhour Construction Co.,
E.Lansing, Mich.
Herbert J. Elkins,
State Paving Corp.,
Hollywood, Fla.
ESCO Corp., Portland, Ore.
E.D. Etnyre & Co., James A. Nelson,
Oregon, Ill.
Euclid, Inc.,
Division of White Motor Corporation,
Cleveland, Ohio
Edward E. Evans, Baton Rouge, La.
**Expanded Shale,
Clay and Slate Institute,**
Washington, D.C.

Fay, Spofford & Thorndike, Inc.,
Boston, Mass.
Faylor-Middlecreek, Inc.,
Winfield, Pa.
Fenton G. Keyes Associates,
Providence, R.I.
Florida Transportation Builders'
Assn., Inc., Tallahassee, Fla.

Fort Chiswell Construction
Corporation, Max Meadows, Va.
Frenzel Construction Co.,
Glenview, Ill.
Fromherz Engineers, Inc.,
New Orleans, La.
Frontier Rock & Sand, Inc.,
Anchorage, Alaska

Gallagher Asphalt Corp.,
Thornton, Ill.
Gannett Fleming Corddry
and Carpenter, Inc.,
Harrisburg, Pa.
Gasparini Excavating Co.,
Peckville, Pa.
Gates Engineering Co.,
Beckley, W.Va.
George & Lynch, Inc.,
New Castle, Delaware
General Electric Credit Corp.,
Stanford, Conn.
William W. Gibb,
The Interstate Amiesite Corp.,
Concordville, Pa.
W.R. Gibbs,
Black & Veatch Consulting Engineers,
Kansas City, Mo.
Gogebic County Road Commission,
Bessemer, Mich.
J.O. Goodman,
Ontario Trucking Association,
Rexdale, Ontario, Canada

Gomaco Corp.,
Ida Grove, Iowa
Goodkind & O'Dea, Inc.,
Clifton, N.J.
Goodyear Tire & Rubber Co.,
W.L. Minor, Vice President,
Akron, Ohio
W.R. Grace & Co.,
Construction Products Div.,
Chicago, Ill.
The Great Lakes Construction Co.,
Cleveland, Ohio
Homer C. Greene,
South Florida Grassing, Inc.,
Hobe Sound, Fla.
Greiner Engineering Sciences, Inc.,
Tampa, Fla.
T.P. Groome Contractor, Inc.,
Fayette, Miss.
Franklin N. Groves,
S.J. Groves & Sons Co.,
Minneapolis, Minn.
William E. Guill, Carthage, Ill.

J.A. Hadley Construction Co., Inc.,
Humboldt, Tenn.
W.L. Hailey and Company, Inc.,
Nashville, Tenn.
Hall & Barber, Inc.,
Cambridge, Ohio
John A. Hall & Company, Inc.,
Roanoke, Va.
H.C. Hanson Construction Co., Inc.,
Bowling Green, Ky.
Warren L. Hardin,
Trego County Engineer,
WaKeeney, Kan.
William E. Hardy, Exec. Sec.,
The Maryland Highways
Contractors Assn., Inc.,
Baltimore, Md.

R.D. Harlow, Schramm, Inc.,
West Chester, Pa.
Frederic R. Harris, Inc.,
New York, N.Y.
Hazelet & Erdal, Louisville, Ky.
The Heffner Construction Co.,
Celina, Ohio
Heltzel Co., Warren, Ohio
Milton A. Hendrickson,
Hendrickson Bros., Inc.,
Valley Stream, N.Y.
Hendrickson Manufacturing Co.,
Lyons, Ill.
The Henley-Lundgren Co.,
Shrewsbury, Mass.
Higgerson-Buchanan, Inc.,
Chesapeake, Va.
Highway Pavers, Inc.,
Milwaukee, Wis.
Highway Supply Corp., Jessup, Md.
Highway Users Federation for
Safety & Mobility,
Washington, D.C.
Hinkle Contracting Corporation,
Paris, Ky.
Robert S. Holmes, Eno Foundation for
Transportation, Inc., Westport, Conn.
Howard, Needles, Tammen
& Bergendoff, Kansas City, Kan.;
Havertord, Pa.; Minneapolis, Minn.
Hubbard Construction Co.,
Orlando, Fla.
Huron County Road Commission,
Bad Axe, Mich.
C.P. Hutcheson, Nashville, Tenn.

Idaho Transportation Dept.,
Boise, Idaho
George J. Igel & Co.,
Columbus, Ohio
Illinois Road Builders' Assn.,
Chicago, Ill.
Independence Excavating, Inc.,
Independence, Ohio
Indiana Toll Road Commission,
South Bend, Ind.
Industrial Credit Company,
St. Paul, Minn.

Ingersoll-Rand Co.,
Woodcliff Lake, N.J.
International Harvester Co.,
Pay Line Division,
Schaumburg, Ill.
Interstate Safety Service, Inc.,
Clarks Summit, Pa.
Iowa Manufacturing Co.,
Cedar Rapids, Iowa
Iosco County Road Commission,
East Tawas, Mich.
ITT Industrial Credit Company,
St. Paul, Minn.

JJ & V Construction Corp.,
Swansea, Mass.
Jackson County Road
Commissioners, Jackson, Mich.
Wiley N. Jackson Co., Roanoke, Va.
Johnson, Depp & Quisenberry,
Owensboro, Ky.

Joy Manufacturing Co.,
Montgomeryville, Pa.
Jurgensen Construction Co.,
Albuquerque, N.M.
P.C. Job, L.B. Smith Metropolitan, Inc.,
Wallington, N.J.

Paul J. Kaiser, P.E.,
Van Buren County Road Commission,
Lawrence, Mich.
Emmett H. Karrer, Prof. Emeritus,
Ohio State University, Dublin, Ohio
Sam Karrh, Vulcan Iron Works Inc.,
West Palm Beach, Fla.
J.T. Keliher, Inc.,
S.Williamsport, Pa.
Wendel F. Kent,
Wendel Kent & Co., Inc.,
Sarasota, Fla.
Kentucky Assn. of
Highway Contractors, Frankfort, Ky.
Kentucky Road Oiling, Inc.,
Lexington, Ky.
Keyes Associates, Providence, R.I.

Shinko Kikegawa, Nippon Hodo Co.,
Tokyo, Japan
George S. Koch, Hartford, Conn.
Koch Construction Co.,
Greenfield, Mass.
Koehring Road Division,
Springfield, Ohio
Arthur J. Kosmatka, President,
Stoehr Grading Company, Inc.,
New Berlin, Wis.
Edward Kraemer & Sons, Inc.,
Plain, Wis.
Kral, Zepf, Freitag & Associates,
Cincinnati, Ohio
Les Kuzmick, Cushion Cut, Inc.,
Harbor City, Calif.

Laidlaw Contracting Co., Inc.,
Mobile, Ala.
Lanford Brothers Co., Inc.,
Roanoke, Va.
Ledbetter Bros., Inc.,
Nelson Magee, Vice Pres., Rome, Ga.
James F. Leware, Leware-Hill, Inc.,
Leesburg, Fla.

Richard Lightholder, McMurray, Pa.
C.W. Littleton, Hardrives Co.,
Ft. Lauderdale, Fla.
A.B. Long, Knoxville, Tenn.
H-E Lowdermilk Co., Englewood, Colo.
Joseph H. Looper,
Howard, Needles, Tammen & Bergendoff,
Milwaukee, Wis.

Macomb County Road Commission,
Mt. Clemens, Mich.
John E. Maloy, James H. Maloy, Inc.,
Loudonville, N.Y.
K.G. Marks, Inc., Port Huron, Mich.
Norman G. Marks,
Richardson, Gordon and Assoc.,
Pittsburgh, Pa.
Martin-Marietta Aggregates,
New York, N.Y.
H.F. Mason Equipment Corp.,
Lakeland, Fla; Hialeah, Fla.;
Fort Myers, Fla.
Massey-Ferguson, Inc.,
Des Moines, Iowa
Mexam, Inc., North Highlands, Ca.
V.O. Menuez & Son, Inc.,
General Contractors, Millersburg, Ohio
Harold L. Michael,
West Lafayette, Ind.
Michigan Tractor & Machinery Co.,
Novi, Mich.
Milburn Brothers, Inc.,
Mt. Prospect, Ill.
Miller-Valentine Corp.,
Dayton, Ohio
Mississippi Road Builders' Assn.,
Jackson, Miss.
Barton S. Mitchell,
E. Stewart Mitchell, Inc.,
Baltimore, Md.

Modjeski & Masters, Harrisburg, Pa.
Monger Brothers Contractors,
Harrisonburg, Va.
J.Robert Moore,
Harland Bartholomew & Assoc.,
Memphis, Tenn.
Morrison-Maierle, Inc., Helena, Mont.
John P. Moss, Leeds, Ala.
Mehdi Muhit, Tehran, Iran

A.K. McBride Construction Company,
Fort Smith, Ark.
M.H. McCartney,
McCartney Construction Co.,
Gadsden, Ala.
J.E. "Red" McCracken,
Bethlehem, Pa.
William R. McGrath,
Raymond Parish & Pine,
Tarrytown, N.Y.
McGeorge Contracting Company,
Pine Bluff, Ark.
McKay Contractors, Inc.,
Chicago, Ill.
McKnight Construction Co.,
Commerce, Texas
J.J. McTague,
Fauber Construction Co., Inc.,
Lafayette, Ind.

Robert M. Nady, Nevada, Iowa
**National Asphalt Pavement
Association,** Riverdale, Md.
**National Corrugated Steel Pipe
Association,** Schiller Park, Ill.
National Crushed Stone Assn.,
Washington, D.C.
National Limestone Institute,
Washington, D.C.

National Slag Association,
Alexandria, Va.
Nickell, Inc., Columbia, Tenn.
Gilbert H. Nolte,
C.J. Langenfelder & Son, Inc.,
Baltimore, Md.
W.J. Noonan, Jr.,
Noonan Construction Co., Inc.,
Pensacola, Fla.

Oklahoma Road Builders' Assn.,
Oklahoma City, Okla.
Oman Construction Co.,
Nashville, Tenn.
**Ottawa County Board of
County Road Commissioners,**
Grand Haven, Mich.
R.Stanton Over,
Gwin Engineers, Inc., Altoona, Pa.

H.M. Pafford,
Dixie Concrete Service, Inc.,
Waycross, Ga.
Paolo Salce & Co.,
Elmwood Park, Ill.
**Parsons, Brinckerhoff,
Quade & Douglas,** New York, N.Y.
The Peirce Construction Co.,
Holland, Ohio
E.J. Peltier,
Sverdrup & Parcel and Assoc.,
St. Louis, Mo.
Pendleton Construction Corporation,
Wytheville, Va.
Gordon F. Penick,
Lee Hy Paving Corp.,
Richmond, Va.

Penoyer Contracting Co., Inc.,
Clearfield, Pa.
Carl L. Penzel, President,
Penzel Construction Co., Inc.,
Jackson, Mo.
Perini Corporation, Framingham, Mass.
Richard E. Phillippi, Inc.,
Wytheville, Va.
William S. Pollard,
W.S. Pollard Consultants,
Memphis, Tenn.
Portland Cement Assn., Skokie, Ill.
**Post, Buckley, Schuh &
Jernigan, Inc.,** Miami, Fla.
Power Curbers, Inc., Salisbury, N.C.
E.S. Preston, Columbus, Ohio
Purcell Associates, Hartford, Conn.

W.E. Quicksall & Assoc., Inc.,
New Philadelphia, Ohio
Paul J. Rach, Inc.,
Lutherville, Md.
Ratrie, Robbins & Schweizer, Inc.,
Baltimore, Md.
RayGo Inc., Minneapolis, Minn.
H.W. Reece, Scandia, Kan.
Reed & Kuhn, Inc., Elysburg, Pa.
John B. Reese, The Reese Companies,
Napoleon, Ohio
B.E. Reichenbach, Inc.,
Selinsgrove, Pa.
Republic Contracting Corp.,
Columbia, S.C.
Republic Steel Corp.,
Drainage Products Division,
Canton, Ohio
Rexnord, Inc., Milwaukee, Wis.
Reynolds Bros. Inc., Canton, Mass.
Charles Riebe Construction Co.,
Palmerton, Pa.
Rieth-Riley Construction Co., Inc.,
Goshen, Ind.

Rignani Associates, Inc.,
Camp Hill, Pa.
Louis C. Ripa,
Porter and Ripa Assoc., Inc.,
Morristown, N.J.
Rissler & McMurry Co.,
Casper, Wyoming
Roads & Streets Magazine,
Chicago, Ill.
Rock Excavators, Inc., Amherst, Va.
Rockwell International,
Off-Highway Products Division,
Troy, Mich.
John W. Rogers, Pres. & Treasurer,
Bates & Rogers Construction Corp.,
Chicago, Ill.
Rogers Bridge Company, Inc.,
Waycross, Ga.
Bernard H. Rottinghaus,
Howard, Needles, Tammen & Bergendoff,
Minneapolis, Minn.
Royal Industries, Signal Division,
Los Angeles, Ca.

San Marco Contracting Co.,
St. Augustine, Fla.
Sanders & Thomas, Inc.,
Pottstown, Pa.
Paul C. Sandy,
Stanley Consultants, Inc.,
Muscatine, Iowa
H.E. Sargent, Inc., Stillwater, Me.
Scarborough Grassing, Inc.,
Brooksville, Fla.
Ammon Schreur,
Pickitt & Schreur, Inc., Allegan, Mich.
Howard E. Schwark,
Kankakee County Supt. of Highways,
Kankakee, Ill.
Scott Bridge Co., Inc.,
Opelika, Ala.
Donald H. Selvage, Inc.,
Amherst, Va.
Shaffer, Johnston,
Lichtenwalter & Assoc., Inc.,
Mansfield, Ohio
Tadao Shimizu,
The Nippon Road Co., Ltd.,
Tokyo, Japan
H.C. Shirley, Dickerson, Inc.,
Monroe, N.C.
Site Preparation, Inc.,
Nashville, Tenn.
Harry T. Skelly, Supt.,
Cumberland, Md.
J. Paul Skelly,
James J. Skelly, Inc., Media, Pa.
Skokie Valley Asphalt Co.,
Des Plaines, Ill.
Frank K. Smith,
F.K. & F.M. Smith Co.,
Washington, D.C.
John W. Smith,
Menard County Supt. of Highways,
Petersburg, Ill.
L.B. Smith, Inc., Camp Hill, Pa.
Wilbur S. Smith,
Wilbur Smith and Assoc.,
Columbia, S.C.

James Snowden,
J.W. Snowden Construction Co.,
Hattiesburg, Miss.
Soiltest, Inc., Evanston, Ill.
Southeastern Asphalt Co.,
Tallahassee, Fla.
Southern Concrete Construction Co.,
Albany, Ga.
Southern Roadbuilders, Inc.,
Augusta, Ga.
H.A. Spalding, Inc., Hazard, Ky.
Stabler Construction Co.,
Harrisburg, Pa.
Stafford Construction, Inc.,
Lubbock, Texas
Donald B. Stafford,
Clemson University, Clemson, S.C.
Stahl Construction Co., Dekalb, Ill.
Standard Industries, Inc.,
Tulsa, Ok.
Richard R. Stander,
Mansfield Asphalt Paving Co.,
Mansfield, Ohio
Starrett Paving Corp.,
Marlborough, Mass.
H.F. Starn, Merchantville, N.J.
Herbert Storch, Storch Engineers,
Florham Park, N.J.
S. Hammond Story Agency, Inc.,
Atlanta, Ga.
Stow Manufacturing Co.,
Binghamton, N.Y.
D.M. Stoltzfus & Son, Inc.,
Talmage, Pa.
J.P. Strother Const., Co., Inc.,
Ottumwa, Iowa
Summers-Taylor, Inc.,
Elizabethton, Tenn.
Sweeney Bros., Inc.,
Johnson Creek, Wis.
Bill Swisher, Oklahoma City, Okla.
Sugden Inc., Novi, Mich.

Taylor, Wiseman & Taylor, Moorestown, N.J.
Teal Construction Inc., Dover, Del.
Nello L. Teer, Jr., Durham, N.C.
Marvin V. Templeton & Sons Inc., Lynchburg, Va.
Tennessee Road Builders' Assn., Nashville, Tenn.
Terex Division of General Motors, Hudson, Ohio
Thomas, Bennett & Hunter, Inc., Westminister, Md.
J.W. Thompson, Jr., Thompson-Arthur Paving Co., Greensboro, N.C.
3M Company, St. Paul, Minn.
Frank Tidwell, Tidwell Construction Co., Douglasville, Ga.

James H. Tiller, Galion Manufacturing Co., Division of Dresser Industries, Inc., Galion, Ohio
Tippits-Abbett-McCarthy-Stratton, New York, N.Y.; Washington, D.C.
Roland G. Tiracorda, Madera, Pa.
Charley Toppino & Sons, Inc., Key West, Fla.
A.B. Torrence & Co., Inc., Elkton, Va.
Sam Torrence, Couch Construction Co., Dothan, Ala.
Troxler Asphalt Co., Inc., Washington, D.C.
Tudor Engineering Company, San Francisco, Ca.
Tyo & Fleisher, Harrisburg, Pa.

URS Corporation, San Mateo, Ca.
United States Steel Corporation, Richard S. Fountain, Manager-Construction Marketing, Pittsburgh, Pa.

Ralph Van Brimmer, P.E., Summit Co. Engineer, Akron, Ohio
Vecellio & Grogan, Inc., Beckley, W.Va.
C.E. Vick, Kimley-Horn & Assoc., Inc., Raleigh, N.C.
ViPond & ViPond, Inc., Hollidaysburg, Pa.
Virginia Road Builders Assn., Richmond, Va.

WABCO Construction & Mining Equipment Group, Peoria, Ill. (An American-Standard Company)
G.A. & F.C. Wagman, Inc., York, Pa.
Arthur Walker, Jr., Mount Sterling, Ky.
Walsh Contracting Corp., Attleboro, Mass.
The Warner & Swazey Co., Solon, Ohio
Warren Brothers Co., Birmingham, Ala., Division of Ashland Oil, Inc.
Wayne County Board of Road Commissioners, Detroit, Mich.
Robert L. Weaver, Orlando, Fla.
Westenhoff & Novick, Inc., Chicago, Ill.
Westinghouse Credit Corp., Pittsburgh, Pa.
James G. Whitaker, Jr., Whitaker Contracting Corp., Guntersville, Ala.

Whitman Requardt & Assoc., Baltimore, Md.
Arthur L. Wiesenberger, President, A.L. Wiesenberger Assoc., Inc., Allentown, Pa.
The Whitaker-Merrell Co., Columbus, Ohio
George M. Williams, Lagona Hills, Calif.
H.J. Williams Co., Inc., York, Pa.
Charles E. Wiles, Flint, Mich.
John E. Wiley, Washington, D.C.
Wilson & Company, Engineers & Architects, Salina, Kan.
Wisconsin Road Builders Association, Madison, Wis.
Wright Brothers Construction Co., Inc., Shelbyville, Tenn.
Wright Contracting Company, Columbus, Ga.
A Distinguished Lifetime Member